POEMS OF HENRY WADSWORTH LONGFELLOW

THE CROWELL POETS

Under the editorship of Lillian Morrison

POEMS OF JOHN KEATS
Selected by Stanley Kunitz

POEMS OF HENRY WADSWORTH LONGFELLOW
Selected by Edmund Fuller

POEMS OF EDGAR ALLAN POE
Selected by Dwight Macdonald

POEMS OF WILLIAM SHAKESPEARE
Selected by Lloyd Frankenberg

POEMS OF ALFRED, LORD TENNYSON
Selected by Ruth Greiner Rausen

POEMS OF WALT WHITMAN
Selected by Lawrence Clark Powell

POEMS OF WILLIAM WORDSWORTH
Selected by Elinor Parker

POEMS OF

HENRY WADSWORTH

LONGFELLOW

Selected by Edmund Fuller

ETCHINGS BY

John Ross and Clare Romano Ross

THOMAS Y. CROWELL COMPANY

NEW YORK

L. C. Card AC67-10072

CONTENTS

POEMS OF HENRY WADSWORTH LONGFELLOW

Or caravans that from Bassora's
gate with west
ward steps depa
or Mecca's
pilgrims conf
of fate and re

INTRODUCTION

THERE ARE two images of the man Henry Wadsworth Longfellow. Due to the fondness of textbooks and reference works for picturing great men in their late years, the most familiar is that of a strong, kindly, venerable face with a thick white beard. His snowy hair falls in careless abundance over his ears and collar. This is the poet at the height of fame, among the most loved in his lifetime of all writers who have ever lived.

A sharply contrasting picture is conjured up by literary historians and biographers who have revived modern interest in the heritage of American letters. This one is of a dashing young man, newly arrived in Cambridge, Massachusetts, at barely thirty years of age, to assume the Smith professorship of modern languages at Harvard. He had been appointed to that post of prestige two years earlier and granted the right to spend the intervening time in Europe —his second such sojourn—enriching his mastery of continental languages and literature. The signs of the romantic rambler were on him—he strode about Cambridge in clothes of bright colors and exotic fabrics that were the talk of that seat of Puritan tradition.

He was not yet an established poet but was already outwardly his time's ideal figure of one: curly-haired and glamorously garbed. True, he soon settled into the Cambridge scene; the dress became more subdued, but he continued to sport a cane and a broad-brimmed hat, though by way of concession both were black.

In his Harvard classroom he held students spellbound.

He opened doors into languages and led his classes to the rich literature, old and new, to be found in each of them, making this wealth of reading the incentive for the mastery of tongues. He told stories and read aloud, in a voice melodious and expressive, with the gifts of an actor. He kindled the love of languages, made the special quality of each stand out, and whipped up eagerness for this study, relatively new on American shores. The grind of teaching—inescapable in languages (though he seemed to have experienced little of it)—was conducted by the lesser men of the department. Longfellow was the inspirer. Meanwhile, away from the college, at nearby Craigie House in Cambridge, the poet—as distinguished from the teacher—was working and developing his skills.

This young man is eager, romantic. The old man of the other image is tranquil—but with a tranquility reached after sorrow and physical suffering. It was ripeness he attained, in the sense of Shakespeare's words, "Ripeness is all"—the fulfilled use of his talents within their natural limits, which is as much as a man can achieve.

Longfellow was born on February 27, 1807, in Portland, Maine, of stock as old in New England as oldness can be reckoned in a world so new. Stephen Longfellow, his father, was a lawyer and wanted Henry to become the same —the literary interests the boy showed early were acceptable as an amateur devotion so long as he had some solid calling with which to earn his livelihood. Reluctantly but dutifully the youth was preparing to read law when the unanticipated came to his rescue.

Henry had attended the new Bowdoin College, near

home, a classmate (1825) of Nathaniel Hawthorne, whom he was to know better in later years when both were literary figures. A year after his graduation the college decided to establish a chair of modern languages, a forward-looking act at that time in American education, especially praiseworthy in so new an institution. The chair was offered to Longfellow, though he was only nineteen and had no proficiency in languages, with the understanding that he would spend some three years in Europe equipping himself for the post. Longfellow accepted eagerly. Two things are striking about this event: the informality of the academic approach to language studies; and the obvious natural gift that Longfellow possessed, for he virtually absorbed the principal languages of Europe, in this and his later trip, by travel, walking, talking, reading, and a minimum of formal study. He mastered French, Spanish, Italian, German, and some of the Scandinavian tongues, chiefly by wandering about and plunging himself into the lives of which they were the voices. He also made forays into Finnish literature, principally through German translations.

In 1829 he took up his duties at Bowdoin, also serving as librarian. The other fruits of his travel and study, emerging in the next few years, included numerous essays on European languages and literature, translations of poetry, some language textbooks, and a book of travel sketches, in the manner of Washington Irving, called *Outre-Mer*, which won him many readers, for such works were popular. Then, in 1834, came the invitation from Harvard, which took him abroad again.

Meanwhile, in 1831, he had married Mary Storer Potter, of Portland. She accompanied him on the return to Europe, but what began as a romantic idyl for the couple became his first tragedy. Mary Longfellow died in Rotterdam, in 1835, of complications following a miscarriage. The young professor's second European visit turned into a sorrowful journey.

When he assumed his duties at Harvard, he began as well a productive career as a writer—of both poetry and prose. Among the early works was a prose romance, *Hyperion* (1839), which won a wide audience. It reflected, thinly disguised in conventional romantic trappings, the unpromising early period of his courtship of his second wife, in Switzerland. In the same year appeared his first volume of poems, *Voices of the Night*, generally admired by public and critics alike—even by Poe, who later became one of the few hostile contemporary critics of Longfellow.

In 1843 he married Frances Elizabeth Appleton, a Boston girl, whose wealthy father bought Craigie House as a gift for the couple. It proved to be an ideally happy union.

In 1854, Longfellow resigned from his professorship—a blessed relief from what he called "the great Prairie of a teacher's life"—and devoted himself solely to poetry, insofar as a rising tide of visitors, and of letters demanding everything from a simple autograph to criticism of manuscripts, would let him.

Craigie House became a focus of pilgrimage. Friends, near and far, resorted to it often—one of them was Charles Dickens, who described the poet as "a remarkably handsome and notable-looking man." Visiting celebrities always must be brought to see the poet—sometimes even royalty, such as Dom Pedro II, Emperor of Brazil. Often the visitors were wholly unannounced, turning up on the doorstep of a man too kind to rebuff them.

A variety of testimonials shows the emotional response his poems could call forth in all sorts and conditions of men. King Leopold I of Belgium was so moved by *Evangeline* that he had the word "Atchafalaya" cut on a seal. It was the name of the lake on which Evangeline and her questing lover passed close by each other unknowingly—a happening that impressed the king as immensely like the tricks of life. In China a mandarin had "The Psalm of Life" engraved on an ivory fan. Students in Alpine Innsbruck hailed the mere German translator of "Excelsior" as a hero.

The Longfellows had six children—two sons, four daughters—and suffered the sorrow of losing one of them—Fanny, named for her mother—when she was little more than a year old.

Theirs was considered a blessed household, hospitable haven to friends of many countries, the marvel of all who knew it for its idyllic family happiness. This was the high good fortune which the ancient Greeks thought wise to conceal from their jealous gods. William Dean Howells wrote that once, as he and Oliver Wendell Holmes were passing Craigie House, Dr. Holmes remarked that he always "trembled to look at it" because "those who lived there had their happiness so perfect that no change"—of those changes that must surely come—"could fail to be for the worse."

Very soon after that remark the change came. On July 9, 1861, Fanny Appleton Longfellow was sitting near an open window, engaged in the poignant task of sealing up packets containing locks of hair of her two daughters. Whether ignited by a spark spit off from a match or by a drop of hot sealing wax, her light dress suddenly became an envelope of flame. Longfellow who was asleep in the next room, his study, was roused by her screams, rushed to try to save her, and in the effort was severely burned on the face and hands. Fanny, her agony briefly relieved by anaesthesia, slipped into coma the next day and died. The poet was too ill from his own burns to attend her funeral.

The anguish of his loss was so bitter that he held it largely locked within, but it was known to his family and close friends, who read the pain in his eyes and his silences. That tragedy is glanced at only obliquely in his poems until, eighteen years later, it found voice in the beautiful sonnet "The Cross of Snow" (p. 142).

He moved, now, toward the quiet years. The white beard, so identified with that period, was a by-product of the tragedy—the severe burn scars on his face made shaving impossible. He worked at his craft of verse until the end—honored and loved—dying in 1882 at the age of seventy-five.

The man, the beloved, courteous person that was Longfellow, ranks high in esteem. How are we to evaluate the poet?

Time, which shuffles reputations, sometimes taking a man's work in and out of fashion more than once over a long period, has dealt with Longfellow in extremes. In his lifetime he became the best-known, most read, most beloved living poet in the world. Possibly no other ever had such popular esteem. It was not a cheap popularity, for the age had not been cheapened. The admiration was not from simple men and women only, but also from his peers, fellow poets, public figures, king and commoner alike. He became his age's symbol of the poet—the ideal figure of his craft—and at the same time he was a literary ambassador from America to Europe. The Royal Spanish Academy made him a member. Oxford and Cambridge bestowed degrees upon him. He was the first American poet to achieve a memorial in the Poets' Corner in Westminster Abbey. Of course, no one is unanimously admired; there were a few who belittled him, but their voices were overwhelmed in the general acclaim.

Longfellow was good-natured about such harsh criticism as he did receive—though it hurt. In his *Table Talk* he remarks: "Many critics are like woodpeckers, who instead of enjoying the fruit and shadow of a tree, hop incessantly around the trunk, pecking holes in the bark to discover some little worm or other."

Some objected to his use of the long, hard-to-manage hexameter line in *Evangeline*—relatively uncommon in English poetry. Longfellow liked it and used it in other poems, though never again so ambitiously. He amused himself by writing a couplet combining the six-footed line with the five-footed one so much more widely employed:

In Hexameter sings serenely a Harvard Professor;
In Pentameter him damns censorious Poe.

At its height in his lifetime, the fame which he enjoyed was extravagant. Correction was certain to come. It came in an almost equal and opposite reaction, as if by some artistic analogy to Newton's laws of motion. The lack of es-

teem into which his work had declined by the early dec-
ades of the present century was as extravagant as the one-
time idolatry. For some years now, a new correction has
been in progress, a move toward a more balanced appraisal,
in spite of the fact that the mood, manner, and content of
Longfellow's poetry are as remote as possible from today's
fashions in poetry.

Longfellow is a good poet—not a great one. Arnold Ben-
nett called him "the chief minor poet of the English language"—far from faint praise if read rightly. The phrase
attributes to him a rank of no small dignity when we remember that major poets are rare.

Both the excess of praise and the extreme reaction from
it were results of qualities apart from his performance as
poet. He struck a chord to which his era was attuned—as
ours decidedly is not—a chord composed of notes of optimism, confidence, faith, sentiment, serenity, gentility, and
simple moral fervor. Because of these qualities, many loved
him who would have done so even had his verse been less
skillful. Because of these same qualities, many in our own
time dislike him, even though at his best he is a fine, easy,
natural craftsman.

It is true that his virtues are close to his vices. He wrote
occasionally some very bad verse in which his natural sentiment, affirmative spirit, and moral earnestness degenerated
into mawkish sentimentality, too-easy optimism, and sen-
tentious moralizing. But those who judge the man by these
poems fail to measure him by his whole body of work, on
which every writer is entitled to be judged, and blind
themselves to what is sound in his philosophy, moving in
his feelings, and excellent in his craftsmanship.

[*8*]

Van Wyck Brooks, in *The Flowering of New England*, began the rehabilitation of Longfellow's poetic reputation: "Everything that passed into his mind turned into music and pictures. . . . He was an innovator in metres and rhythms; he introduced new moods of feeling; he touched the world with a magic that was mild but unmistakable."

"Mild" is the key word. Longfellow is not a poet of intensity, passion, or high tragedy. His nature is gentle and temperate. He celebrates the best in man and in life because that is what he loves—not because he does not know that the rest is there. Some reputations have been built since by celebrating the worst. Longfellow was a student of Dante, wrote some fine sonnets and other poems about him. His Harvard lectures did much to make Dante known in this country, and still more did his superior translation of the entire *Divine Comedy*. A man capable of this knowledgeable service to Dante is not a man whose observation of life is limited to shallows.

Emotional, often spontaneous in the sense that poems occasionally welled from him in swift improvisation (as did "The Arrow and the Song," p. 42), he was, in words of his own, a poet "whose songs gushed from his heart." He lacked—as did so different a writer as Mark Twain—a sure sense of discrimination between his best and his weakest work, although the gap that separates best from worst is large.

Yet he did criticize himself, was never complacent in his greatest success. The sonnet "Mezzo Cammin" (p. 140), written at thirty-five though not published until after his death, lamented:

Half of my life has gone, and I have let
The years slip from me and have not fulfilled
The aspiration of my youth . . . .

More significant still are the lines of his own old age,
cloaked in the character of his Michael Angelo:

Alas, how little
Of all I dreamed of has my hand achieved!

And he feels still

The fever to accomplish some great work
That will not let us sleep. I must go on
Until I die.

Longfellow is dismissed by some in this latter day simply
for wanting his poems to mean something. A much-quoted
line from Archibald MacLeish's "Ars Poetica" proclaims,
"A poem should not mean/But be." But where is it written
that a poem cannot both mean *and* be? The great poets
have always been passionately concerned to have their
poems mean.

Longfellow is also a poet-storyteller; indeed, that is one
of his most prolific and best veins in both long and short
works. His finest narrative achievements are in the brilli-
antly diversified *Tales of a Wayside Inn*. His poetic dramas
—*The Spanish Student, The Golden Legend*, and others—
fail in that they are more lyrical than dramatic, curiously
static compared to the movement of the narrative poems.
Yet they contain some fine passages—particularly the late,
incomplete drama which he called *Michael Angelo: A Fragment*, several excerpts from which are included in this

selection. It presents some of Longfellow's ripened views about art.

We have seen that he traveled much in his youth, absorbed foreign cultures, and made their literary treasures known in America. He used old-world materials freely, but he is also an intensely, consciously American poet. No other has used American Indian lore as extensively, together with chronicles of the English and European settlers. The novelist Henry James praised the remarkable "harmony" in which Longfellow's " 'European' and his native culture kept house together." *Tales of a Wayside Inn* exemplifies that harmony supremely in its diversity from "Paul Revere's Ride" to "King Robert of Sicily" to the technical brilliance of the long "Saga of King Olaf." Yet those wholly home-inspired poems, *The Courtship of Miles Standish, Evangeline*, and especially *Hiawatha*, have passed into American "mythology," more important now as myth or legend than as poetry.

In his boyhood in Portland Longfellow acquired a love of the sea, and through all his years felt a profound responsiveness to its ebb and flow, its violence and calm, its weed and wrack, transforming these often into metaphors of life.

Longfellow was a superb translator, from Spanish, Swedish, Danish, German, Anglo-Saxon, French, and Italian. During the first years of his Harvard lectures, translation helped to sustain and develop his poetic gift and to protect it from being damaged by the burden of academic work. He once compared translation to "running a ploughshare through the soil of one's mind; a thousand gems of thought start up . . . which otherwise might have lain and rotted in the ground." His masterpiece of translation was the whole of Dante's *Divine Comedy*—one of the best English versions. The sonnet sequence, "Divina Commedia," and some of the other poems included here reflect that large labor.

The attempt in this book is to represent Longfellow in his best and most characteristic veins. The very sentimental or preachy poems have been omitted, with the exception of one or two that have been household favorites for years and from which tags of verse are much quoted. Obviously in a slender book those narrative poems that are slender books in themselves cannot be included. *Evangeline* is represented only by its brief prologue. That, and a short Indian poem, "To the Driving Cloud," exhibit Longfellow's use of the hexameter line. *Hiawatha* is represented by a single episode which displays the poet's sensitivity to nature. Its cadences were inspired by the rhythm of the Finnish epic *Kalevala*. *Tales of a Wayside Inn* has yielded five widely varied stories.

"Excelsior" and "The Village Blacksmith," not distinguished poems, are included to represent his experiments in this ballad vein. "I have broken new ground in a new field," he wrote to a friend about his poems in this style. Their naïveté is that of the folk form on which they are based.

Several of his anti-slavery poems and two against war have been grouped with "The Jewish Cemetery at Newport" and "In the Churchyard at Cambridge" as "Songs of Principle" (the editor's, not the poet's, phrase), because they are good in themselves and also show Longfellow's rare direct comment on social problems. He was not a militant poet. That he felt deeply about these matters is evident in the poems themselves, though the hot zealots of the abolitionist movement were not satisfied with them. "In the Churchyard at Cambridge" is a profound poem whose cryptic lines strike at moral complacency. It is one of his best poems and one of the most neglected.

This selection, then, in the word of the ancient Greek anthologist Meleager, is a "garland" of Longfellow—a poet of skill, serenity, and noble spirit, uneven but at his best not to be let go.

SONGS OF MEMORY
AND OTHER LYRICS

A Dutch Picture

Simon Danz has come home again,
    From cruising about with his buccaneers;
He has singed the beard of the King of Spain,
And carried away the Dean of Jaen
    And sold him in Algiers.

In his house by the Maese, with its roof of tiles,
    And weathercocks flying aloft in air,
There are silver tankards of antique styles,
Plunder of convent and castle, and piles
    Of carpets rich and rare.

In his tulip-garden there by the town,
    Overlooking the sluggish stream,
With his Moorish cap and dressing-gown,
The old sea-captain, hale and brown,
    Walks in a waking dream.

A smile in his gray mustachio lurks
    Whenever he thinks of the King of Spain,
And the listed tulips look like Turks,
And the silent gardener as he works
    Is changed to the Dean of Jaen.

The windmills on the outermost
    Verge of the landscape in the haze,
To him are towers on the Spanish coast,

With whiskered sentinels at their post,
  Though this is the river Maese.

But when the winter rains begin,
  He sits and smokes by the blazing brands,
And old seafaring men come in,
Goat-bearded, gray, and with double chin,
  And rings upon their hands.

They sit there in the shadow and shine
  Of the flickering fire of the winter night;
Figures in color and design
Like those by Rembrandt of the Rhine,
  Half darkness and half light.

And they talk of ventures lost or won,
  And their talk is ever and ever the same,
While they drink the red wine of Tarragon,
From the cellars of some Spanish Don,
  Or convent set on flame.

Restless at times with heavy strides
  He paces his parlor to and fro;
He is like a ship that at anchor rides,
And swings with the rising and falling tides,
  And tugs at her anchor-tow.

Voices mysterious far and near,
  Sound of the wind and sound of the sea,
Are calling and whispering in his ear,

"Simon Danz! Why stayest thou here?
  Come forth and follow me!"

So he thinks he shall take to the sea again
  For one more cruise with his buccaneers,
To singe the beard of the King of Spain,
And capture another Dean of Jaen
  And sell him in Algiers.

The Fire of Drift-Wood

WE sat within the farm-house old,
  Whose windows, looking o'er the bay,
Gave to the sea-breeze damp and cold
  An easy entrance, night and day.

Not far away we saw the port,
  The strange, old-fashioned, silent town,
The lighthouse, the dismantled fort,
  The wooden houses, quaint and brown.

We sat and talked until the night,
  Descending, filled the little room;
Our faces faded from the sight,
  Our voices only broke the gloom.

We spake of many a vanished scene,
  Of what we once had thought and said,
Of what had been, and might have been,
  And who was changed, and who was dead;

And all that fills the hearts of friends,
  When first they feel, with secret pain,
Their lives thenceforth have separate ends,
  And never can be one again;

The first slight swerving of the heart,
  That words are powerless to express,

And leave it still unsaid in part,
    Or say it in too great excess.

The very tones in which we spake
    Had something strange, I could but mark;
The leaves of memory seemed to make
    A mournful rustling in the dark.

Oft died the words upon our lips,
    As suddenly, from out the fire
Built of the wreck of stranded ships,
    The flames would leap and then expire.

And, as their splendor flashed and failed,
    We thought of wrecks upon the main,
Of ships dismasted, that were hailed
    And sent no answer back again.

The windows, rattling in their frames,
    The ocean, roaring up the beach,
The gusty blast, the bickering flames,
    All mingled vaguely in our speech;

Until they made themselves a part
    Of fancies floating through the brain,
The long-lost ventures of the heart,
    That send no answers back again.

O flames that glowed! O hearts that yearned!
    They were indeed too much akin,
The drift-wood fire without that burned,
    The thoughts that burned and glowed within.

My Lost Youth

O<small>FTEN</small> I think of the beautiful town
    That is seated by the sea;
Often in thought go up and down
The pleasant streets of that dear old town,
    And my youth comes back to me.
        And a verse of a Lapland song
        Is haunting my memory still:
        "A boy's will is the wind's will,
And the thoughts of youth are long, long thoughts."

I can see the shadowy lines of its trees,
    And catch, in sudden gleams,
The sheen of the far-surrounding seas,
And islands that were the Hesperides
    Of all my boyish dreams.
        And the burden of that old song,
        It murmurs and whispers still:
        "A boy's will is the wind's will,
And the thoughts of youth are long, long thoughts."

I remember the black wharves and the slips,
    And the sea-tides tossing free;
And Spanish sailors with bearded lips,
And the beauty and mystery of the ships,
    And the magic of the sea.
        And the voice of that wayward song
        Is singing and saying still:
        "A boy's will is the wind's will,
And the thoughts of youth are long, long thoughts."

I remember the bulwarks by the shore,
   And the fort upon the hill;
The sunrise gun, with its hollow roar,
The drum-beat repeated o'er and o'er,
   And the bugle wild and shrill.
      And the music of that old song
      Throbs in my memory still:
      "A boy's will is the wind's will,
And the thoughts of youth are long, long thoughts."

I remember the sea-fight far away,
   How it thundered o'er the tide!
And the dead captains, as they lay
In their graves, o'erlooking the tranquil bay
   Where they in battle died.
      And the sound of that mournful song
      Goes through me with a thrill:
      "A boy's will is the wind's will,
And the thoughts of youth are long, long thoughts."

I can see the breezy dome of groves,
   The shadows of Deering's Woods;
And the friendship old and the early loves
Come back with a Sabbath sound, as of doves
   In quiet neighborhoods.
      And the verse of that sweet old song,
      It flutters and murmurs still:
      "A boy's will is the wind's will,
And the thoughts of youth are long, long thoughts."

I remember the gleams and glooms that dart
   Across the school-boy's brain;

The song and the silence in the heart,
That in part are prophecies, and in part
    Are longings wild and vain.
        And the voice of that fitful song
        Sings on, and is never still:
        "A boy's will is the wind's will,
And the thoughts of youth are long, long thoughts."

There are things of which I may not speak;
    There are dreams that cannot die;
There are thoughts that make the strong heart weak,
And bring a pallor into the cheek,
    And a mist before the eye.
        And the words of that fatal song
        Come over me like a chill:
        "A boy's will is the wind's will,
And the thoughts of youth are long, long thoughts."

Strange to me now are the forms I meet
    When I visit the dear old town;
But the native air is pure and sweet,
And the trees that o'ershadow each well-known street,
    As they balance up and down,
        Are singing the beautiful song,
        Are sighing and whispering still:
        "A boy's will is the wind's will,
And the thoughts of youth are long, long thoughts."

And Deering's Woods are fresh and fair,
    And with joy that is almost pain
My heart goes back to wander there,

And among the dreams of the days that were,
   I find my lost youth again.
      And the strange and beautiful song,
      The groves are repeating it still:
      "A boy's will is the wind's will,
And the thoughts of youth are long, long thoughts."

Vox Populi

WHEN Mazárvan the Magician
    Journeyed westward through Cathay,
Nothing heard he but the praises
    Of Badoura on his way.

But the lessening rumor ended
    When he came to Khaledan,
There the folk were talking only
    Of Prince Camaralzaman.

So it happens with the poets:
    Every province hath its own;
Camaralzaman is famous
    Where Badoura is unknown.

Seaweed

WHEN descends on the Atlantic
    The gigantic
Storm-wind of the equinox,
Landward in his wrath he scourges
    The toiling surges,
Laden with seaweed from the rocks:

From Bermuda's reefs; from edges
    Of sunken ledges,
In some far-off, bright Azore;
From Bahama, and the dashing,
    Silver-flashing
Surges of San Salvador.

From the tumbling surf, that buries
    The Orkneyan skerries,
Answering the hoarse Hebrides;
And from wrecks of ships, and drifting
    Spars, uplifting
On the desolate, rainy seas;—

Ever drifting, drifting, drifting
    On the shifting
Currents of the restless main;
Till in sheltered coves, and reaches
    Of sandy beaches,
All have found repose again.

So when storms of wild emotion
            Strike the ocean
Of the poet's soul, ere long
From each cave and rocky fastness,
            In its vastness,
Floats some fragment of a song:

From the far-off isles enchanted,
            Heaven has planted
With the golden fruit of Truth;
From the flashing surf, whose vision
            Gleams Elysian
In the tropic clime of Youth;

From the strong Will, and the Endeavor
            That forever
Wrestle with the tides of Fate;
From the wreck of Hopes far-scattered,
            Tempest-shattered,
Floating waste and desolate;—

Ever drifting, drifting, drifting
            On the shifting
Currents of the restless heart;
Till at length in books recorded,
            They, like hoarded
Household words, no more depart.

Daylight and Moonlight

In broad daylight, and at noon,
Yesterday I saw the moon
Sailing high, but faint and white,
As a school-boy's paper kite.

In broad daylight yesterday,
I read a Poet's mystic lay;
And it seemed to me at most
As a phantom, or a ghost.

But at length the feverish day
Like a passion died away,
And the night, serene and still,
Fell on village, vale, and hill.

Then the moon, in all her pride,
Like a spirit glorified,
Filled and overflowed the night
With revelations of her light.

And the Poet's song again
Passed like music through my brain;
Night interpreted to me
All its grace and mystery.

Hymn to the Night

I HEARD the trailing garments of the Night
   Sweep through her marble halls!
I saw her sable skirts all fringed with light
   From the celestial walls!

I felt her presence by its spell of might,
   Stoop o'er me from above;
The calm, majestic presence of the Night,
   As of the one I love.

I heard the sounds of sorrow and delight,
   The manifold, soft chimes,
That fill the haunted chambers of the Night,
   Like some old poet's rhymes.

From the cool cisterns of the midnight air
   My spirit drank repose;
The fountain of perpetual peace flows there,—
   From those deep cisterns flows.

O holy Night! from thee I learn to bear
   What man has borne before!
Thou layest thy finger on the lips of Care,
   And they complain no more.

Peace! Peace! Orestes-like I breathe this prayer!
   Descend with broad-winged flight,
The welcome, the thrice-prayed for, the most fair,
   The best-beloved Night!

Daybreak

A WIND came up out of the sea,
And said, "O mists, make room for me."

It hailed the ships, and cried, "Sail on,
Ye mariners, the night is gone."

And hurried landward far away,
Crying, "Awake! it is the day."

It said unto the forest, "Shout!
Hang all your leafy banners out!"

It touched the wood-bird's folded wing.
And said, "O bird, awake and sing"

And o'er the farms, "O chanticleer,
Your clarion blow; the day is near."

It whispered to the fields of corn,
"Bow down, and hail the coming morn."

It shouted through the belfry-tower,
"Awake, O bell! proclaim the hour."

It crossed the churchyard with a sigh,
And said, "Not yet! in quiet lie."

Serenade

FROM THE SPANISH STUDENT

STARS of the summer night!
    Far in yon azure deeps,
Hide, hide your golden light!
    She sleeps!
My lady sleeps!
    Sleeps!

Moon of the summer night!
    Far down yon western steeps,
Sink, sink in silver light!
    She sleeps!
My lady sleeps!
    Sleeps!

Wind of the summer night!
    Where yonder woodbine creeps,
Fold, fold thy pinions light!
    She sleeps!
My lady sleeps!
    Sleeps!

Dreams of the summer night!
    Tell her, her lover keeps
Watch! while in slumbers light
    She sleeps!
My lady sleeps!
    Sleeps!

Sand of the Desert in an Hour-Glass

A HANDFUL of red sand, from the hot clime
    Of Arab deserts brought,
Within this glass becomes the spy of Time,
    The minister of Thought.

How many weary centuries has it been
    About those deserts blown!
How many strange vicissitudes has seen,
    How many histories known!

Perhaps the camels of the Ishmaelite
    Trampled and passed it o'er,
When into Egypt from the patriarch's sight
    His favorite son they bore.

Perhaps the feet of Moses, burnt and bare,
    Crushed it beneath their tread,
Or Pharaoh's flashing wheels into the air
    Scattered it as they sped;

Or Mary, with the Christ of Nazareth
    Held close in her caress,
Whose pilgrimage of hope and love and faith
    Illumed the wilderness;

Or anchorites beneath Engaddi's palms
    Pacing the Dead Sea beach,
And singing slow their old Armenian psalms
    In half-articulate speech;

Or caravans, that from Bassora's gate
    With westward steps depart;
Or Mecca's pilgrims, confident of Fate,
    And resolute in heart!

These have passed over it, or may have passed!
    Now in this crystal tower
Imprisoned by some curious hand at last,
    It counts the passing hour.

And as I gaze, these narrow walls expand;—
    Before my dreamy eye
Stretches the desert with its shifting sand,
    Its unimpeded sky.

And borne aloft by the sustaining blast,
    This little golden thread
Dilates into a column high and vast,
    A form of fear and dread.

And onward, and across the setting sun,
    Across the boundless plain,
The column and its broader shadow run,
    Till thought pursues in vain.

The vision vanishes! These walls again
    Shut out the lurid sun,
Shut out the hot, immeasurable plain;
    The half-hour's sand is run!

The Chamber Over the Gate

Is it so far from thee
Thou canst no longer see,
In the Chamber over the Gate,
That old man desolate,
Weeping and wailing sore
For his son, who is no more?
   O Absalom, my son!

Is it so long ago
That cry of human woe
From the walled city came,
Calling on his dear name,
That it has died away
In the distance of to-day?
   O Absalom, my son!

There is no far or near,
There is neither there nor here,
There is neither soon nor late,
In that Chamber over the Gate,
Nor any long ago
To that cry of human woe,
   O Absalom, my son!

From the ages that are past
The voice sounds like a blast,
Over seas that wreck and drown,
Over tumult of traffic and town;

And from ages yet to be
Come the echoes back to me,
    O Absalom, my son!

Somewhere at every hour
The watchman on the tower
Looks forth, and sees the fleet
Approach of the hurrying feet
Of messengers, that bear
The tidings of despair.
    O Absalom, my son!

He goes forth from the door,
Who shall return no more.
With him our joy departs;
The light goes out in our hearts;
In the Chamber over the Gate
We sit disconsolate.
    O Absalom, my son!

That 't is a common grief
Bringeth but slight relief;
Ours is the bitterest loss,
Ours is the heaviest cross;
And forever the cry will be
"Would God I had died for thee,
    O Absalom, my son!"

The Ropewalk

In that building, long and low,
With its windows all a-row,
    Like the port-holes of a hulk,
Human spiders spin and spin,
Backward down their threads so thin
    Dropping, each a hempen bulk.

At the end, an open door;
Squares of sunshine on the floor
    Light the long and dusky lane;
And the whirring of a wheel,
Dull and drowsy, makes me feel
    All its spokes are in my brain.

As the spinners to the end
Downward go and reascend,
    Gleam the long threads in the sun;
While within this brain of mine
Cobwebs brighter and more fine
    By the busy wheel are spun.

Two fair maidens in a swing,
Like white doves upon the wing,
    First before my vision pass;
Laughing, as their gentle hands
Closely clasp the twisted strands,
    At their shadow on the grass.

Then a booth of mountebanks,
With its smell of tan and planks,
    And a girl poised high in air
On a cord, in spangled dress,
With a faded liveliness,
    And a weary look of care.

Then a homestead among farms,
And a woman with bare arms
    Drawing water from a well;
As the bucket mounts apace,
With it mounts her own fair face,
    As at some magician's spell.

Then an old man in a tower,
Ringing loud the noontide hour,
    While the rope coils round and round
Like a serpent at his feet,
And again, in swift retreat,
    Nearly lifts him off the ground.

Then within a prison-yard,
Faces fixed, and stern, and hard,
    Laughter and indecent mirth;
Ah! it is the gallows-tree!
Breath of Christian charity,
    Blow, and sweep it from the earth!

Then a school-boy, with his kite
Gleaming in a sky of light,
    And an eager, upward look;

Steeds pursued through lane and field;
Fowlers with their snares concealed;
   And an angler by a brook.

Ships rejoicing in the breeze,
Wrecks that float o'er unknown seas,
   Anchors dragged through faithless sand;
Sea-fog drifting overhead,
And, with lessening line and lead,
   Sailors feeling for the land.

All these scenes do I behold,
These, and many left untold,
   In that building long and low;
While the wheel goes round and round,
With a drowsy, dreamy sound,
   And the spinners backward go.

God's-Acre

I LIKE that ancient Saxon phrase, which calls
    The burial-ground God's-Acre! It is just;
It consecrates each grave within its walls,
    And breathes a benison o'er the sleeping dust.

God's-Acre! Yes, that blessed name imparts
    Comfort to those who in the grave have sown
The seed that they had garnered in their hearts,
    Their bread of life, alas! no more their own.

Into its furrows shall we all be cast,
    In the sure faith, that we shall rise again
At the great harvest, when the archangel's blast
    Shall winnow, like a fan, the chaff and grain.

Then shall the good stand in immortal bloom,
    In the fair gardens of that second birth;
And each bright blossom mingle its perfume
    With that of flowers, which never bloomed on
      earth.

With thy rude ploughshare, Death, turn up the sod,
    And spread the furrow for the seed we sow;
This is the field and Acre of our God,
    This is the place where human harvests grow.

Snow-Flakes

Out of the bosom of the Air,
　Out of the cloud-folds of her garments shaken,
Over the woodlands brown and bare,
　Over the harvest-fields forsaken,
　　Silent, and soft, and slow
　　Descends the snow.

Even as our cloudy fancies take
　Suddenly shape in some divine expression,
Even as the troubled heart doth make
　In the white countenance confession,
　　The troubled sky reveals
　　The grief it feels.

This is the poem of the air,
　Slowly in silent syllables recorded;
This is the secret of despair,
　Long in its cloudy bosom hoarded,
　　Now whispered and revealed
　　To wood and field.

The Arrow and the Song

I SHOT an arrow into the air,
It fell to earth, I knew not where;
For, so swiftly it flew, the sight
Could not follow it in its flight.

I breathed a song into the air,
It fell to earth, I knew not where;
For who has sight so keen and strong,
That it can follow the flight of song?

Long, long afterward, in an oak
I found the arrow, still unbroke;
And the song, from beginning to end,
I found again in the heart of a friend.

The Rainy Day

THE day is cold, and dark, and dreary;
It rains, and the wind is never weary;
The vine still clings to the mouldering wall,
But at every gust the dead leaves fall,
   And the day is dark and dreary.

My life is cold, and dark, and dreary;
It rains, and the wind is never weary;
My thoughts still cling to the mouldering Past,
But the hopes of youth fall thick in the blast,
   And the days are dark and dreary.

Be still, sad heart! and cease repining;
Behind the clouds is the sun still shining;
Thy fate is the common fate of all,
Into each life some rain must fall,
   Some days must be dark and dreary.

Aftermath

WHEN the summer fields are mown,
When the birds are fledged and flown,
   And the dry leaves strew the path:
With the falling of the snow,
With the cawing of the crow,
Once again the fields we mow
   And gather in the aftermath.

Not the sweet, new grass with flowers
Is this harvesting of ours;
   Not the upland clover bloom;
But the rowen mixed with weeds,
Tangled tufts from marsh and meads,
Where the poppy drops its seeds
   In the silence and the gloom.

The Day Is Done

THE day is done, and the darkness
    Falls from the wings of Night,
As a feather is wafted downward
    From an eagle in his flight.

I see the lights of the village
    Gleam through the rain and the mist,
And a feeling of sadness comes o'er me
    That my soul cannot resist:

A feeling of sadness and longing,
    That is not akin to pain,
And resembles sorrow only
    As the mist resembles the rain.

Come, read to me some poem,
    Some simple and heartfelt lay,
That shall soothe this restless feeling,
    And banish the thoughts of day.

Not from the grand old masters,
    Not from the bards sublime,
Whose distant footsteps echo
    Through the corridors of Time.

For, like strains of martial music,
    Their mighty thoughts suggest

Life's endless toil and endeavor;
    And to-night I long for rest.

Read from some humbler poet,
    Whose songs gushed from his heart,
As showers from the clouds of summer,
    Or tears from the eyelids start;

Who, through long days of labor,
    And nights devoid of ease,
Still heard in his soul the music
    Of wonderful melodies.

Such songs have power to quiet
    The restless pulse of care,
And come like the benediction
    That follows after prayer.

Then read from the treasured volume
    The poem of thy choice,
And lend to the rhyme of the poet
    The beauty of thy voice.

And the night shall be filled with music,
    And the cares, that infest the day,
Shall fold their tents, like the Arabs,
    And as silently steal away.

To the Driving Cloud

Gloomy and dark art thou, O chief of the mighty Omahas;
Gloomy and dark as the driving cloud, whose name thou
    hast taken!
Wrapped in thy scarlet blanket, I see thee stalk through the
    city's
Narrow and populous streets, as once by the margin of
    rivers
Stalked those birds unknown, that have left us only their
    footprints.
What, in a few short years, will remain of thy race but the
    footprints?

How canst thou walk these streets, who hast trod the green
    turf of the prairies?
How canst thou breathe this air, who hast breathed the
    sweet air of the mountains?
Ah! 't is in vain that with lordly looks of disdain thou dost
    challenge
Looks of disdain in return, and question these walls and
    these pavements,
Claiming the soil for thy hunting-grounds, while down-
    trodden millions
Starve in the garrets of Europe, and cry from its caverns
    that they, too,
Have been created heirs of the earth, and claim its division!

Back, then, back to thy woods in the regions west of the
    Wabash!

There as a monarch thou reignest. In autumn the leaves of
    the maple
Pave the floors of thy palace-halls with gold, and in summer
Pine-trees waft through its chambers the odorous breath of
    their branches.
There thou art strong and great, a hero, a tamer of horses!
There thou chasest the stately stag on the banks of the
    Elkhorn,
Or by the roar of the Running-Water, or where the Omaha
Calls thee, and leaps through the wild ravine like a brave of
    the Blackfeet!

Hark! what murmurs arise from the heart of those moun-
    tainous deserts?
Is it the cry of the Foxes and Crows, or the mighty Behe-
    moth,
Who, unharmed, on his tusks once caught the bolts of the
    thunder,
And now lurks in his lair to destroy the race of the red man?
Far more fatal to thee and thy race than the Crows and the
    Foxes,
Far more fatal to thee and thy race than the tread of Be-
    hemoth,
Lo! the big thunder-canoe, that steadily breasts the Mis-
    souri's
Merciless current! and yonder, afar on the prairies, the
    camp-fires
Gleam through the night; and the cloud of dust in the gray
    of the daybreak
Marks not the buffalo's track, nor the Mandan's dexterous
    horse-race;

It is a caravan, whitening the desert where dwell the Ca-
manches!
Ha! how the breath of these Saxons and Celts, like the blast
of the east-wind,
Drifts evermore to the west the scanty smokes of thy
wigwams!

THIS is the forest primeval. The murmuring pines and the
    hemlocks,
Bearded with moss, and in garments green, indistinct in the
    twilight,
Stand like Druids of eld, with voices sad and prophetic,
Stand like harpers hoar, with beards that rest on their bos-
    oms.
Loud from its rocky caverns, the deep-voiced neighboring
    ocean
Speaks, and in accents disconsolate answers the wail of the
    forest.

  This is the forest primeval; but where are the hearts that
      beneath it
Leaped like the roe, when he hears in the woodland the
    voice of the huntsman?
Where is the thatch-roofed village, the home of Acadian
    farmers,—
Men whose lives glided on like rivers that water the wood-
    lands,
Darkened by shadows of earth, but reflecting an image of
    heaven?
Waste are those pleasant farms, and the farmers forever
    departed!
Scattered like dust and leaves, when the mighty blasts of
    October
Seize them, and whirl them aloft, and sprinkle them far o'er
    the ocean,

Naught but tradition remains of the beautiful village of
    Grand-Pré.

  Ye who believe in affection that hopes and endures, and
        is patient,
Ye who believe in the beauty and strength of woman's
        devotion,
List to the mournful tradition still sung by the pines of the
        forest;
List to a Tale of Love in Acadie, home of the happy.

The Tide Rises, the Tide Falls

THE tide rises, the tide falls,
The twilight darkens, the curlew calls;
Along the sea-sands damp and brown
The traveller hastens toward the town,
   And the tide rises, the tide falls.

Darkness settles on roofs and walls,
But the sea, the sea in the darkness calls;
The little waves, with their soft, white hands,
Efface the footprints in the sands,
   And the tide rises, the tide falls.

The morning breaks; the steeds in their stalls
Stamp and neigh, as the hostler calls;
The day returns, but nevermore
Returns the traveller to the shore,
   And the tide rises, the tide falls.

STORY IN SONG

The Bell of Atri

FROM TALES OF A WAYSIDE INN

At Atri in Abruzzo, a small town
Of ancient Roman date, but scant renown,
One of those little places that have run
Half up the hill, beneath a blazing sun,
And then sat down to rest, as if to say,
"I climb no farther upward, come what may,"—
The Re Giovanni, now unknown to fame,
So many monarchs since have borne the name,
Had a great bell hung in the market-place,
Beneath a roof, projecting some small space
By way of shelter from the sun and rain.
Then rode he through the streets with all his train,
And, with the blast of trumpets loud and long,
Made proclamation, that whenever wrong
Was done to any man, he should but ring
The great bell in the square, and he, the King,
Would cause the Syndic to decide thereon.
Such was the proclamation of King John.

How swift the happy days in Atri sped,
What wrongs were righted, need not here be said.
Suffice it that, as all things must decay,
The hempen rope at length was worn away,
Unravelled at the end, and, strand by strand,
Loosened and wasted in the ringer's hand,
Till one, who noted this in passing by,
Mended the rope with braids of briony,

So that the leaves and tendrils of the vine
Hung like a votive garland at a shrine.

By chance it happened that in Atri dwelt
A knight, with spur on heel and sword in belt,
Who loved to hunt the wild-boar in the woods,
Who loved his falcons with their crimson hoods,
Who loved his hounds and horses, and all sports
And prodigalities of camps and courts; —
Loved, or had loved them; for at last, grown old,
His only passion was the love of gold.

He sold his horses, sold his hawks and hounds,
Rented his vineyards and his garden-grounds,
Kept but one steed, his favorite steed of all,
To starve and shiver in a naked stall,
And day by day sat brooding in his chair,
Devising plans how best to hoard and spare.

At length he said: "What is the use or need
To keep at my own cost this lazy steed,
Eating his head off in my stables here,
When rents are low and provender is dear?
Let him go feed upon the public ways;
I want him only for the holidays."
So the old steed was turned into the heat
Of the long, lonely, silent, shadeless street;
And wandered in suburban lanes forlorn,
Barked at by dogs, and torn by brier and thorn.

One afternoon, as in that sultry clime
It is the custom in the summer time,
With bolted doors and window-shutters closed,
The inhabitants of Atri slept or dozed;
When suddenly upon their senses fell
The loud alarm of the accusing bell!
The Syndic started from his deep repose,
Turned on his couch, and listened, and then rose
And donned his robes, and with reluctant pace
Went panting forth into the market-place,
Where the great bell upon its cross-beams swung,
Reiterating with persistent tongue,
In half-articulate jargon, the old song:
"Some one hath done a wrong, hath done a wrong!"

But ere he reached the belfry's light arcade
He saw, or thought he saw, beneath its shade,
No shape of human form of woman born,
But a poor steed dejected and forlorn,
Who with uplifted head and eager eye
Was tugging at the vines of briony.
"Domeneddio!" cried the Syndic straight,
"This is the Knight of Atri's steed of state!
He calls for justice, being sore distressed,
And pleads his cause as loudly as the best."

Meanwhile from street and lane a noisy crowd
Had rolled together like a summer cloud,
And told the story of the wretched beast
In five-and-twenty different ways at least,

With much gesticulation and appeal
To heathen gods, in their excessive zeal.
The Knight was called and questioned; in reply
Did not confess the fact, did not deny;
Treated the matter as a pleasant jest,
And set at naught the Syndic and the rest,
Maintaining, in an angry undertone,
That he should do what pleased him with his own.

And thereupon the Syndic gravely read
The proclamation of the King; then said:
"Pride goeth forth on horseback grand and gay,
But cometh back on foot, and begs its way;
Fame is the fragrance of heroic deeds,
Of flowers of chivalry and not of weeds!
These are familiar proverbs; but I fear
They never yet have reached your knightly ear.
What fair renown, what honor, what repute
Can come to you from starving this poor brute?
He who serves well and speaks not, merits more
Than they who clamor loudest at the door.
Therefore the law decrees that as this steed
Served you in youth, henceforth you shall take heed
To comfort his old age, and to provide
Shelter in stall, and food and field beside."

The Knight withdrew abashed; the people all
Led home the steed in triumph to his stall.
The King heard and approved, and laughed in glee,
And cried aloud: "Right well it pleaseth me!
Church-bells at best but ring us to the door;

But go not in to mass; my bell doth more:
It cometh into court and pleads the cause
Of creatures dumb and unknown to the laws;
And this shall make, in every Christian clime,
The Bell of Atri famous for all time."

Belisarius

I AM poor and old and blind;
The sun burns me, and the wind
  Blows through the city gate,
And covers me with dust
From the wheels of the august
  Justinian the Great.

It was for him I chased
The Persians o'er wild and waste,
  As General of the East;
Night after night I lay
In their camps of yesterday;
  Their forage was my feast.

For him, with sails of red,
And torches at mast-head,
  Piloting the great fleet,
I swept the Afric coasts
And scattered the Vandal hosts,
  Like dust in a windy street.

For him I won again
The Ausonian realm and reign,
  Rome and Parthenope;
And all the land was mine

From the summits of Apennine
　　To the shores of either sea.

For him, in my feeble age,
I dared the battle's rage,
　　To save Byzantium's state,
When the tents of Zabergan
Like snow-drifts overran
　　The road to the Golden Gate.

And for this, for this, behold!
Infirm and blind and old,
　　With gray, uncovered head,
Beneath the very arch
Of my triumphal march,
　　I stand and beg my bread!

Methinks I still can hear,
Sounding distinct and near,
　　The Vandal monarch's cry,
As, captive and disgraced,
With majestic step he paced,—
　　"All, all is Vanity!"

Ah! vainest of all things
Is the gratitude of kings;
　　The plaudits of the crowd
Are but the clatter of feet
At midnight in the street,
　　Hollow and restless and loud.

But the bitterest disgrace
Is to see forever the face
    Of the Monk of Ephesus!
The unconquerable will
This, too, can bear;—I still
    Am Belisarius!

The Building of the Ship

BUILD me straight, O worthy Master!
  Stanch and strong, a goodly vessel,
That shall laugh at all disaster,
  And with wave and whirlwind wrestle!"

The merchant's word
Delighted the Master heard;
For his heart was in his work, and the heart
Giveth grace unto every Art.
A quiet smile played round his lips,
As the eddies and dimples of the tide
Play round the bows of ships,
That steadily at anchor ride.
And with a voice that was full of glee,
He answered, "Erelong we will launch
A vessel as goodly, and strong, and stanch
As ever weathered a wintry sea!"
And first with nicest skill and art,
Perfect and finished in every part,
A little model the Master wrought,
Which should be to the larger plan
What the child is to the man,
Its counterpart in miniature;
That with a hand more swift and sure
The greater labor might be brought
To answer to his inward thought.
And as he labored, his mind ran o'er
The various ships that were built of yore,

And above them all, the strangest of all
Towered the Great Harry, crank and tall,
Whose picture was hanging on the wall,
With bows and stern raised high in air,
And balconies hanging here and there,
And signal lanterns and flags afloat,
And eight round towers, like those that frown
From some old castle, looking down
Upon the drawbridge and the moat.
And he said with a smile, "Our ship, I wis,
Shall be of another form than this!"
It was of another form indeed;
Built for freight, and yet for speed,
A beautiful and gallant craft;
Broad in the beam, that the stress of the blast,
Pressing down upon sail and mast,
Might not the sharp bows overwhelm;
Broad in the beam, but sloping aft
With graceful curve and slow degrees,
That she might be docile to the helm,
And that the current of parted seas,
Closing behind with mighty force,
Might aid and not impede her course.

In the ship-yard stood the Master,
With the model of the vessel,
That should laugh at all disaster,
And with wave and whirlwind wrestle!

Covering many a rood of ground,
Lay the timber piled around;

Timber of chestnut, and elm, and oak,
And scattered here and there, with these,
The knarred and crooked cedar knees;
Brought from regions far away,
From Pascagoula's sunny bay,
And the banks of the roaring Roanoke!
Ah! what a wondrous thing it is
To note how many wheels of toil
One thought, one word, can set in motion!
There's not a ship that sails the ocean,
But every climate, every soil,
Must bring its tribute, great or small,
And help to build the wooden wall!

The sun was rising o'er the sea,
And long the level shadows lay,
As if they, too, the beams would be
Of some great, airy argosy,
Framed and launched in a single day.
That silent architect, the sun,
Had hewn and laid them every one,
Ere the work of man was yet begun.
Beside the Master, when he spoke,
A youth, against an anchor leaning,
Listened, to catch his slightest meaning.
Only the long waves, as they broke
In ripples on the pebbly beach,
Interrupted the old man's speech.

Beautiful they were, in sooth,
The old man and the fiery youth!

The old man, in whose busy brain
Many a ship that sailed the main
Was modelled o'er and o'er again;—
The fiery youth, who was to be
The heir of his dexterity,
The heir of his house, and his daughter's hand,
When he had built and launched from land
What the elder head had planned.

"Thus," said he, "will we build this ship!
Lay square the blocks upon the slip,
And follow well this plan of mine.
Choose the timbers with greatest care;
Of all that is unsound beware;
For only what is sound and strong
To this vessel shall belong.
Cedar of Maine and Georgia pine
Here together shall combine.
A goodly frame, and a goodly fame,
And the UNION be her name!
For the day that gives her to the sea
Shall give my daughter unto thee!"

The Master's word
Enraptured the young man heard;
And as he turned his face aside,
With a look of joy and a thrill of pride
Standing before
Her father's door,
He saw the form of his promised bride.
The sun shone on her golden hair,

And her cheek was glowing fresh and fair,
With the breath of morn and the soft sea air.
Like a beauteous barge was she,
Still at rest on the sandy beach,
Just beyond the billow's reach;
But he
Was the restless, seething, stormy sea!

Ah, how skilful grows the hand
That obeyeth Love's command!
It is the heart, and not the brain,
That to the highest doth attain,
And he who followeth Love's behest
Far excelleth all the rest!

Thus with the rising of the sun
Was the noble task begun,
And soon throughout the ship-yard's bounds
Were heard the intermingled sounds
Of axes and of mallets, plied
With vigorous arms on every side;
Plied so deftly and so well,
That, ere the shadows of evening fell,
The keel of oak for a noble ship,
Scarfed and bolted, straight and strong,
Was lying ready, and stretched along
The blocks, well placed upon the slip.
Happy, thrice happy, every one
Who sees his labor well begun,
And not perplexed and multiplied,
By idly waiting for time and tide!

And when the hot, long day was o'er,
The young man at the Master's door
Sat with the maiden calm and still,
And within the porch, a little more
Removed beyond the evening chill,
The father sat, and told them tales
Of wrecks in the great September gales,
Of pirates coasting the Spanish Main,
And ships that never came back again,
The chance and change of a sailor's life,
Want and plenty, rest and strife,
His roving fancy, like the wind,
That nothing can stay and nothing can bind,
And the magic charm of foreign lands,
With shadows of palms, and shining sands,
Where the tumbling surf,
O'er the coral reefs of Madagascar,
Washes the feet of the swarthy Lascar,
As he lies alone and asleep on the turf.
And the trembling maiden held her breath
At the tales of that awful, pitiless sea,
With all its terror and mystery,
The dim, dark sea, so like unto Death,
That divides and yet unites mankind!
And whenever the old man paused, a gleam
From the bowl of his pipe would awhile illume
The silent group in the twilight gloom,
And thoughtful faces, as in a dream;
And for a moment one might mark
What had been hidden by the dark,
That the head of the maiden lay at rest,
Tenderly, on the young man's breast!

Day by day the vessel grew,
With timbers fashioned strong and true,
Stemson and keelson and sternson-knee,
Till, framed with perfect symmetry,
A skeleton ship rose up to view!
And around the bows and along the side
The heavy hammers and mallets plied,
Till after many a week, at length,
Wonderful for form and strength,
Sublime in its enormous bulk,
Loomed aloft the shadowy hulk!
And around it columns of smoke, upwreathing,
Rose from the boiling, bubbling, seething
Caldron, that glowed,
And overflowed
With the black tar, heated for the sheathing.
And amid the clamors
Of clattering hammers,
He who listened heard now and then
The song of the Master and his men:—

"Build me straight, O worthy Master,
    Stanch and strong, a goodly vessel,
That shall laugh at all disaster,
    And with wave and whirlwind wrestle!"

With oaken brace and copper band,
Lay the rudder on the sand,
That, like a thought, should have control
Over the movement of the whole;
And near it the anchor, whose giant hand
Would reach down and grapple with the land,

And immovable and fast
Hold the great ship against the bellowing blast!
And at the bows an image stood,
By a cunning artist carved in wood,
With robes of white, that far behind
Seemed to be fluttering in the wind.
It was not shaped in a classic mould,
Not like a Nymph or Goddess of old,
Or Naiad rising from the water,
But modelled from the Master's daughter!
On many a dreary and misty night,
'T will be seen by the rays of the signal light.
Speeding along through the rain and the dark,
Like a ghost in its snow-white sark,
The pilot of some phantom bark,
Guiding the vessel, in its flight,
By a path none other knows aright!

Behold at last,
Each tall and tapering mast
Is swung into its place;
Shrouds and stays
Holding it firm and fast!

Long ago,
In the deer-haunted forests of Maine,
When upon mountain and plain
Lay the snow,
They fell, — those lordly pines!
Those grand, majestic pines!
'Mid shouts and cheers

The jaded steers,
Panting beneath the goad,
Dragged down the weary, winding road
Those captive kings so straight and tall,
To be shorn of their streaming hair,
And naked and bare,
To feel the stress and the strain
Of the wind and the reeling main,
Whose roar
Would remind them forevermore
Of their native forests they should not see again.

And everywhere
The slender, graceful spars
Poise aloft in the air,
And at the mast-head,
White, blue, and red,
A flag unrolls the stripes and stars.
Ah! when the wanderer, lonely, friendless,
In foreign harbors shall behold
That flag unrolled,
'T will be as a friendly hand
Stretched out from his native land,
Filling his heart with memories sweet and endless!

All is finished! and at length
Has come the bridal day
Of beauty and of strength.
To-day the vessel shall be launched!
With fleecy clouds the sky is blanched,
And o'er the bay,

Slowly, in all his splendors dight,
The great sun rises to behold the sight.

The ocean old,
Centuries old,
Strong as youth, and as uncontrolled,
Paces restless to and fro
Up and down the sands of gold.
His beating heart is not at rest;
And far and wide,
With ceaseless flow,
His beard of snow
Heaves with the heaving of his breast.
He waits impatient for his bride.
There she stands,
With her foot upon the sands,
Decked with flags and streamers gay,
In honor of her marriage day,
Her snow-white signals fluttering, blending,
Round her like a veil descending,
Ready to be
The bride of the gray old sea.

On the deck another bride
Is standing by her lover's side.
Shadows from the flags and shrouds,
Like the shadows cast by clouds,
Broken by many a sudden fleck,
Fall around them on the deck.

The prayer is said
The service read,

The joyous bridegroom bows his head;
And in tears the good old Master
Shakes the brown hand of his son,
Kisses his daughter's glowing cheek
In silence, for he cannot speak,
And ever faster
Down his own the tears begin to run.
The worthy pastor—
The shepherd of that wandering flock,
That has the ocean for its wold,
That has the vessel for its fold,
Leaping ever from rock to rock—
Spake, with accents mild and clear,
Words of warning, words of cheer,
But tedious to the bridegroom's ear.
He knew the chart
Of the sailor's heart,
All its pleasures and its griefs,
All its shallows and rocky reefs,
All those secret currents, that flow
With such resistless undertow,
And lift and drift, with terrible force,
The will from its moorings and its course.
Therefore he spake, and thus said he:—
"Like unto ships far off at sea,
Outward or homeward bound, are we.
Before, behind, and all around,
Floats and swings the horizon's bound,
Seems at its distant rim to rise
And climb the crystal wall of the skies,
And then again to turn and sink,

As if we could slide from its outer brink.
Ah! it is not the sea,
It is not the sea that sinks and shelves,
But ourselves
That rock and rise
With endless and uneasy motion,
Now touching the very skies,
Now sinking into the depths of ocean.
Ah! if our souls but poise and swing
Like the compass in its brazen ring,
Ever level and ever true
To the toil and the task we have to do,
We shall sail securely, and safely reach
The Fortunate Isles, on whose shining beach
The sights we see, and the sounds we hear,
Will be those of joy and not of fear!"

Then the Master,
With a gesture of command,
Waved his hand;
And at the word,
Loud and sudden there was heard,
All around them and below,
The sound of hammers, blow on blow,
Knocking away the shores and spurs.
And see! she stirs!
She starts,—she moves,—she seems to feel
The thrill of life along her keel,
And, spurning with her foot the ground,
With one exulting, joyous bound,
She leaps into the ocean's arms!

And lo! from the assembled crowd
There rose a shout, prolonged and loud,
That to the ocean seemed to say,
"Take her, O bridegroom, old and gray,
Take her to thy protecting arms,
With all her youth and all her charms!"

How beautiful she is! How fair
She lies within those arms, that press
Her form with many a soft caress
Of tenderness and watchful care!
Sail forth into the sea, O ship!
Through wind and wave, right onward steer!
The moistened eye, the trembling lip,
Are not the signs of doubt and fear.

Sail forth into the sea of life,
O gentle, loving, trusting wife,
And safe from all adversity
Upon the bosom of that sea
Thy comings and thy goings be!
For gentleness and love and trust
Prevail o'er angry wave and gust;
And in the wreck of noble lives
Something immortal still survives!

Thou, too, sail on, O Ship of State!
Sail on, O UNION, strong and great!
Humanity with all its fears,
With all the hopes of future years,
Is hanging breathless on thy fate!

We know what Master laid thy keel,
What Workmen wrought thy ribs of steel,
Who made each mast, and sail, and rope,
What anvils rang, what hammers beat,
In what a forge and what a heat
Were shaped the anchors of thy hope!
Fear not each sudden sound and shock,
'T is but the flapping of the sail,
And not a rent made by the gale!
In spite of rock and tempest's roar,
In spite of false lights on the shore,
Sail on, nor fear to breast the sea!
Our hearts, our hopes, are all with thee,
Our hearts, our hopes, our prayers, our tears,
Our faith triumphant o'er our fears,
Are all with thee,—are all with thee!

Paul Revere's Ride

FROM TALES OF A WAYSIDE INN

Listen, my children, and you shall hear
Of the midnight ride of Paul Revere,
On the eighteenth of April, in Seventy-five;
Hardly a man is now alive
Who remembers that famous day and year.

He said to his friend, "If the British march
By land or sea from the town to-night,
Hang a lantern aloft in the belfry arch
Of the North Church tower as a signal light,—
One, if by land, and two, if by sea;
And I on the opposite shore will be,
Ready to ride and spread the alarm
Through every Middlesex village and farm,
For the country-folk to be up and to arm."

Then he said, "Good night!" and with muffled oar
Silently rowed to the Charlestown shore,
Just as the moon rose over the bay,
Where swinging wide at her moorings lay
The Somerset, British man-of-war;
A phantom ship, with each mast and spar
Across the moon like a prison bar,
And a huge black hulk, that was magnified
By its own reflection in the tide.

Meanwhile, his friend, through alley and street,
Wanders and watches with eager ears,
Till in the silence around him he hears
The muster of men at the barrack door,
The sound of arms, and the tramp of feet,
And the measured tread of the grenadiers,
Marching down to their boats on the shore.

Then he climbed the tower of the Old North
    Church,
By the wooden stairs, with stealthy tread,
To the belfry-chamber overhead,
And startled the pigeons from their perch
On the sombre rafters, that round him made
Masses and moving shapes of shade,—
By the trembling ladder, steep and tall,
To the highest window in the wall,
Where he paused to listen and look down
A moment on the roofs of the town,
And the moonlight flowing over all.

Beneath in the churchyard, lay the dead,
In their night-encampment on the hill,
Wrapped in silence so deep and still
That he could hear, like a sentinel's tread,
The watchful night-wind, as it went
Creeping along from tent to tent,
And seeming to whisper, "All is well!"
A moment only he feels the spell
Of the place and the hour, and the secret dread

Of the lonely belfry and the dead;
For suddenly all his thoughts are bent
On a shadowy something far away,
Where the river widens to meet the bay,—
A line of black that bends and floats
On the rising tide, like a bridge of boats.

Meanwhile, impatient to mount and ride,
Booted and spurred, with a heavy stride
On the opposite shore walked Paul Revere.
Now he patted his horse's side,
Now gazed at the landscape far and near,
Then, impetuous, stamped the earth,
And turned and tightened his saddle-girth;
But mostly he watched with eager search
The belfry-tower of the Old North Church,
As it rose above the graves on the hill,
Lonely and spectral and sombre and still.
And lo! as he looks, on the belfry's height
A glimmer, and then a gleam of light!
He springs to the saddle, the bridle he turns,
But lingers and gazes, till full on his sight
A second lamp in the belfry burns!

A hurry of hoofs in a village street,
A shape in the moonlight, a bulk in the dark,
And beneath, from the pebbles, in passing, a spark
Struck out by a steed flying fearless and fleet:
That was all! And yet, through the gloom and the
    light,

The fate of a nation was riding that night;
And the spark struck out by that steed, in his
  flight,
Kindled the land into flame with its heat.

He has left the village and mounted the steep,
And beneath him, tranquil and broad and deep,
Is the Mystic, meeting the ocean tides;
And under the alders that skirt its edge,
Now soft on the sand, now loud on the ledge,
Is heard the tramp of his steed as he rides.

It was twelve by the village clock,
When he crossed the bridge into Medford town.
He heard the crowing of the cock,
And the barking of the farmer's dog,
And felt the damp of the river fog,
That rises after the sun goes down.

It was one by the village clock,
When he galloped into Lexington.
He saw the gilded weathercock
Swim in the moonlight as he passed,
And the meeting-house windows, blank and bare,
Gaze at him with a spectral glare,
As if they already stood aghast
At the bloody work they would look upon.

It was two by the village clock,
When he came to the bridge in Concord town.
He heard the bleating of the flock,

And the twitter of birds among the trees,
And felt the breath of the morning breeze
Blowing over the meadows brown.
And one was safe and asleep in his bed
Who at the bridge would be first to fall,
Who that day would be lying dead,
Pierced by the British musket-ball.

You know the rest. In the books you have read,
How the British Regulars fired and fled,—
How the farmers gave them ball for ball,
From behind each fence and farm-yard wall,
Chasing the red-coats down the lane,
Then crossing the fields to emerge again
Under the trees at the turn of the road,
And only pausing to fire and load.

So through the night rode Paul Revere;
And so through the night went his cry of alarm
To every Middlesex village and farm,—
A cry of defiance and not of fear,
A voice in the darkness, a knock at the door,
And a word that shall echo forevermore!
For, borne on the night-wind of the Past,
Through all our history, to the last,
In the hour of darkness and peril and need,
The people will waken and listen to hear
The hurrying hoof-beats of that steed,
And the midnight message of Paul Revere.

The Legend of Rabbi Ben Levi

FROM TALES OF A WAYSIDE INN

Rabbi Ben Levi, on the Sabbath, read
A volume of the Law, in which it said,
"No man shall look upon my face and live."
And as he read, he prayed that God would give
His faithful servant grace with mortal eye
To look upon His face and yet not die.

Then fell a sudden shadow on the page,
And lifting up his eyes, grown dim with age,
He saw the Angel of Death before him stand,
Holding a naked sword in his right hand.
Rabbi Ben Levi was a righteous man,
Yet through his veins a chill of terror ran.
With trembling voice he said, "What wilt thou
    here?"
The Angel answered, "Lo! the time draws near
When thou must die; yet first, by God's decree,
Whate'er thou askest shall be granted thee."
Replied the Rabbi, "Let these living eyes
First look upon my place in Paradise."

Then said the Angel, "Come with me and look."
Rabbi Ben Levi closed the sacred book,
And rising, and uplifting his gray head,
"Give me thy sword," he to the Angel said,
"Lest thou shouldst fall upon me by the way."
The Angel smiled and hastened to obey,

Then led him forth to the Celestial Town,
And set him on the wall, whence, gazing down,
Rabbi Ben Levi, with his living eyes,
Might look upon his place in Paradise.

Then straight into the city of the Lord
The Rabbi leaped with the Death-Angel's sword,
And through the streets there swept a sudden breath
Of something there unknown, which men call death.
Meanwhile the Angel stayed without, and cried,
"Come back!" To which the Rabbi's voice replied,
"No! in the name of God, whom I adore,
I swear that hence I will depart no more!"

Then all the Angels cried, "O Holy One,
See what the son of Levi here hath done!
The kingdom of Heaven he takes by violence,
And in Thy name refuses to go hence!"
The Lord replied, "My Angels, be not wroth;
Did e'er the son of Levi break his oath?
Let him remain; for he with mortal eye
Shall look upon my face and yet not die."

Beyond the outer wall the Angel of Death
Heard the great voice, and said, with panting breath,
"Give back the sword, and let me go my way."
Whereat the Rabbi paused, and answered, "Nay!
Anguish enough already hath it caused
Among the sons of men." And while he paused
He heard the awful mandate of the Lord
Resounding through the air, "Give back the sword!"

The Rabbi bowed his head in silent prayer,
Then said he to the dreadful Angel, "Swear
No human eye shall look on it again;
But when thou takest away the souls of men,
Thyself unseen, and with an unseen sword,
Thou wilt perform the bidding of the Lord."
The Angel took the sword again, and swore,
And walks on earth unseen forevermore.

Hiawatha's Sailing

FROM THE SONG OF HIAWATHA

GIVE me of your bark, O Birch-tree!
Of your yellow bark, O Birch-tree!
Growing by the rushing river,
Tall and stately in the valley!
I a light canoe will build me,
Build a swift Cheemaun for sailing,
That shall float upon the river,
Like a yellow leaf in Autumn,
Like a yellow water-lily!
    "Lay aside your cloak, O Birch-tree!
Lay aside your white-skin wrapper,
For the Summer-time is coming,
And the sun is warm in heaven,
And you need no white-skin wrapper!"
    Thus aloud cried Hiawatha
In the solitary forest,
By the rushing Taquamenaw,
When the birds were singing gayly,
In the Moon of Leaves were singing,
And the sun, from sleep awaking,
Started up and said, "Behold me!
Gheezis, the great Sun, behold me!"
    And the tree with all its branches
Rustled in the breeze of morning,
Saying, with a sigh of patience,
"Take my cloak, O Hiawatha!"
    With his knife the tree he girdled;

Just beneath its lowest branches,
Just above the roots, he cut it,
Till the sap came oozing outward;
Down the trunk, from top to bottom,
Sheer he cleft the bark asunder,
With a wooden wedge he raised it,
Stripped it from the trunk unbroken.
  "Give me of your boughs, O Cedar!
Of your strong and pliant branches,
My canoe to make more steady,
Make more strong and firm beneath me!"
  Through the summit of the Cedar
Went a sound, a cry of horror,
Went a murmur of resistance;
But it whispered, bending downward,
"Take my boughs, O Hiawatha!"
  Down he hewed the boughs of cedar,
Shaped them straightway to a framework,
Like two bows he formed and shaped them,
Like two bended bows together.
  "Give me of your roots, O Tamarack!
Of your fibrous roots, O Larch-tree!
My canoe to bind together
That the water may not enter,
That the river may not wet me!"
  And the Larch, with all its fibres,
Shivered in the air of morning,
Touched his forehead with its tassels,
Said, with one long sigh of sorrow,
"Take them all, O Hiawatha!"
  From the earth he tore the fibres,

Tore the tough roots of the Larch-tree,
Closely sewed the bark together,
Bound it closely to the framework.

"Give me of your balm, O Fir-tree!
Of your balsam and your resin,
So to close the seams together
That the water may not enter,
That the river may not wet me!"

And the Fir-tree, tall and sombre,
Sobbed through all its robes of darkness,
Rattled like a shore with pebbles,
Answered wailing, answered weeping,
"Take my balm, O Hiawatha!"

And he took the tears of balsam,
Took the resin of the Fir-tree,
Smeared therewith each seam and fissure,
Made each crevice safe from water.

"Give me of your quills, O Hedgehog!
All your quills, O Kagh, the Hedgehog!
I will make a necklace of them,
Make a girdle for my beauty,
And two stars to deck her bosom!"

From a hollow tree the Hedgehog
With his sleepy eyes looked at him,
Shot his shining quills, like arrows,
Saying with a drowsy murmur,
Through the tangle of his whiskers,
"Take my quills, O Hiawatha!"

From the ground the quills he gathered,
All the little shining arrows,
Stained them red and blue and yellow,

With the juice of roots and berries;
Into his canoe he wrought them,
Round its waist a shining girdle,
Round its bows a gleaming necklace,
On its breast two stars resplendent.

Thus the Birch Canoe was builded
In the valley, by the river,
In the bosom of the forest;
And the forest's life was in it,
All its mystery and its magic,
All the lightness of the birch-tree,
All the toughness of the cedar,
All the larch's supple sinews;
And it floated on the river
Like a yellow leaf in Autumn,
Like a yellow water-lily.

Paddles none had Hiawatha,
Paddles none he had or needed,
For his thoughts as paddles served him,
And his wishes served to guide him;
Swift or slow at will he glided,
Veered to right or left at pleasure.

Then he called aloud to Kwasind,
To his friend, the strong man, Kwasind,
Saying, "Help me clear this river
Of its sunken logs and sand-bars."

Straight into the river Kwasind
Plunged as if he were an otter,
Dived as if he were a beaver,
Stood up to his waist in water,
To his arm-pits in the river,

Swam and shouted in the river,
Tugged at sunken logs and branches,
With his hands he scooped the sand-bars,
With his feet the ooze and tangle.
    And thus sailed my Hiawatha
Down the rushing Taquamenaw,
Sailed through all its bends and windings,
Sailed through all its deeps and shallows,
While his friend the strong man, Kwasind,
Swam the deeps, the shallows waded.
    Up and down the river went they,
In and out among its islands,
Cleared its bed of root and sand-bar,
Dragged the dead trees from its channel,
Made its passage safe and certain,
Made a pathway for the people,
From its springs among the mountains,
To the waters of Pauwating,
To the bay of Taquamenaw.

Azrael

FROM TALES OF A WAYSIDE INN

KING Solomon, before his palace gate
At evening, on the pavement tessellate
Was walking with a stranger from the East,
Arrayed in rich attire as for a feast,
The mighty Runjeet-Sing, a learned man,
And Rajah of the realms of Hindostan.
And as they walked the guest became aware
Of a white figure in the twilight air,
Gazing intent, as one who with surprise
His form and features seemed to recognize;
And in a whisper to the king he said:
"What is yon shape, that, pallid as the dead,
Is watching me, as if he sought to trace
In the dim light the features of my face?"

The king looked, and replied: "I know him well;
It is the Angel men call Azrael,
'T is the Death Angel; what hast thou to fear?"
And the guest answered: "Lest he should come near.
And speak to me, and take away my breath!
Save me from Azrael, save me from death!
O king, that hast dominion o'er the wind,
Bid it arise and bear me hence to Ind."

The king gazed upward at the cloudless sky,
Whispered a word, and raised his hand on high,
And lo! the signet-ring of chrysoprase

On his uplifted finger seemed to blaze
With hidden fire, and rushing from the west
There came a mighty wind, and seized the guest
And lifted him from earth, and on they passed,
His shining garments streaming in the blast,
A silken banner o'er the walls upreared,
A purple cloud, that gleamed and disappeared.
Then said the Angel smiling: "If this man
Be Rajah Runjeet-Sing of Hindostan,
Thou hast done well in listening to his prayer;
I was upon my way to seek him there."

A Roman Legend

FROM MORITURI SALUTAMUS

In mediaeval Rome, I know not where,
There stood an image with its arm in air,
And on its lifted finger, shining clear,
A golden ring with the device, "Strike here!"
Greatly the people wondered, though none guessed
The meaning that these words but half expressed,
Until a clerk who at noonday
With downcast eyes was passing on his way,
Paused, and observed the spot, and marked it well,
Whereon the shadow of the finger fell;
And, coming back at midnight, delved, and found
A secret stairway leading underground.
Down this he passed into a spacious hall,
Lit by a flaming jewel on the wall;
And opposite, in threatening attitude,
With bow and shaft a brazen statue stood.
Upon its forehead, like a coronet,
Were these mysterious words of menace set:
"That which I am, I am; my fatal aim
None can escape, not even yon luminous flame!"

Midway the hall was a fair table placed,
With cloth of gold, and golden cups enchased
With rubies, and the plates and knives were gold,
And gold the bread and viands manifold.
Around it, silent, motionless, and sad,
Were seated gallant knights in armor clad,

And ladies beautiful with plume and zone,
But they were stone, their hearts within were stone;
And the vast hall was filled in every part
With silent crowds, stony in face and heart.

Long at the scene, bewildered and amazed,
The trembling clerk in speechless wonder gazed;
Then from the table, by his greed made bold,
He seized a goblet and a knife of gold,
And suddenly from their seats the guests upsprang,
The vaulted ceiling with loud clamors rang,
The archer sped his arrow, at their call,
Shattering the lambent jewel on the wall,
And all was dark around and overhead;—
Stark on the floor the luckless clerk lay dead!

The writer of this legend then records
Its ghostly application in these words:
The image is the Adversary old,
Whose beckoning finger points to realms of gold;
Our lusts and passions are the downward stair
That leads the soul from a diviner air;
The archer, Death; the flaming jewel, Life;
Terrestrial goods, the goblet and the knife;
The knights and ladies, all whose flesh and bone
By avarice have been hardened into stone;
The clerk, the scholar whom the love of pelf
Tempts from his books and from his nobler self.

The scholar and the world! The endless strife,
The discord in the harmonies of life!

The love of learning, the sequestered nooks,
And all the sweet serenity of books;
The market-place, the eager love of gain,
Whose aim is vanity, and whose end is pain!

But why, you ask me, should this tale be told
To men grown old, or who are growing old?
It is too late! Ah, nothing is too late
Till the tired heart shall cease to palpitate.
Cato learned Greek at eighty; Sophocles
Wrote his grand Oedipus, and Simonides
Bore off the prize of verse from his compeers,
When each had numbered more than fourscore years,
And Theophrastus, at fourscore and ten,
Had but begun his "Characters of Men."
Chaucer, at Woodstock with the nightingales,
At sixty wrote the Canterbury Tales;
Goethe at Weimar, toiling to the last,
Completed Faust when eighty years were past.
These are indeed exceptions; but they show
How far the gulf-stream of our youth may flow
Into the arctic regions of our lives,
Where little else than life itself survives
As the barometer foretells the storm
While still the skies are clear, the weather warm,
So something in us, as old age draws near,
Betrays the pressure of the atmosphere.
The nimble mercury, ere we are aware,
Descends the elastic ladder of the air;
The telltale blood in artery and vein
Sinks from its higher levels in the brain;

Whatever poet, orator, or sage
May say of it, old age is still old age.
It is the waning, not the crescent moon;
The dusk of evening, not the blaze of noon;
It is not strength, but weakness; not desire,
But its surcease; not the fierce heat of fire,
The burning and consuming element,
But that of ashes and of embers spent,
In which some living sparks we still discern
Enough to warm, but not enough to burn.

What then? Shall we sit idly down and say
The night hath come; it is no longer day?
The night hath not yet come; we are not quite
Cut off from labor by the failing light;
Something remains for us to do or dare;
Even the oldest tree some fruit may bear;
Not Oedipus Coloneus, or Greek Ode,
Or tales of pilgrims that one morning rode
Out of the gateway of the Tabard Inn,
But other something, would we but begin;
For age is opportunity no less
Than youth itself, though in another dress,
And as the evening twilight fades away
The sky is filled with stars, invisible by day.

The Legend Beautiful

FROM TALES OF A WAYSIDE INN

H<small>ADST</small> thou stayed, I must have fled!"
That is what the Vision said.

In his chamber all alone,
Kneeling on the floor of stone,
Prayed the Monk in deep contrition
For his sins of indecision,
Prayed for greater self-denial
In temptation and in trial;
It was noonday by the dial,
And the Monk was all alone.

Suddenly, as if it lightened,
An unwonted splendor brightened
All within him and without him
In that narrow cell of stone;
And he saw the Blessed Vision
Of our Lord, with light Elysian
Like a vesture wrapped about Him,
Like a garment round Him thrown.

Not as crucified and slain,
Not in agonies of pain,
Not with bleeding hands and feet,
Did the Monk his Master see;
But as in the village street,
In the house or harvest-field,

Halt and lame and blind He healed,
When He walked in Galilee.

In an attitude imploring,
Hands upon his bosom crossed,
Wondering, worshipping, adoring,
Knelt the Monk in rapture lost.
Lord, he thought, in heaven that reignest,
Who am I, that thus thou deignest
To reveal thyself to me?
Who am I, that from the centre
Of thy glory thou shouldst enter
This poor cell, my guest to be?

Then amid his exaltation,
Loud the convent bell appalling,
From its belfry calling, calling,
Rang through court and corridor
With persistent iteration
He had never heard before.
It was now the appointed hour
When alike in shine or shower,
Winter's cold or summer's heat,
To the convent portals came
All the blind and halt and lame,
All the beggars of the street,
For their daily dole of food
Dealt them by the brotherhood;
And their almoner was he
Who upon his bended knee,
Rapt in silent ecstasy

Of divinest self-surrender,
Saw the Vision and the Splendor.
Deep distress and hesitation
Mingled with his adoration;
Should he go or should he stay?
Should he leave the poor to wait
Hungry at the convent gate,
Till the Vision passed away?
Should he slight his radiant guest,
Slight this visitant celestial,
For a crowd of ragged, bestial
Beggars at the convent gate?
Would the Vision there remain?
Would the Vision come again?
Then a voice within his breast
Whispered, audible and clear
As if to the outward ear:
"Do thy duty; that is best;
Leave unto thy Lord the rest!"

Straightway to his feet he started,
And with longing look intent
On the Blessed Vision bent,
Slowly from his cell departed,
Slowly on his errand went.

At the gate the poor were waiting,
Looking through the iron grating,
With the terror in the eye
That is only seen in those
Who amid their wants and woes

Hear the sound of doors that close,
And of feet that pass them by;
Grown familiar with disfavor,
Grown familiar with the savor
Of the bread by which men die!
But to-day, they know not why,
Like the gate of Paradise
Seemed the convent gate to rise,
Like a sacrament divine
Seemed to them the bread and wine.
In his heart the Monk was praying,
Thinking of the homeless poor,
What they suffer and endure;
What we see not, what we see;
And the inward voice was saying:
"Whatsoever thing thou doest
To the least of mine and lowest,
That thou doest unto me!"

Unto me! but had the Vision
Come to him in beggar's clothing,
Come a mendicant imploring,
Would he then have knelt adoring,
Or have listened with derision,
And have turned away with loathing?

Thus his conscience put the question,
Full of troublesome suggestion,
As at length, with hurried pace,
Towards his cell he turned his face.
And beheld the convent bright

With a supernatural light,
Like a luminous cloud expanding
Over floor and wall and ceiling.

But he paused with awe-struck feeling
At the threshold of his door,
For the Vision still was standing
As he left it there before,
When the convent bell appalling,
From its belfry calling, calling,
Summoned him to feed the poor.
Through the long hour intervening
It had waited his return,
And he felt his bosom burn,
Comprehending all the meaning,
When the Blessed Vision said,
"Hadst thou stayed, I must have fled!"

The Sermon of St. Francis

Up soared the lark into the air,
A shaft of song, a winged prayer,
As if a soul released from pain
Were flying back to heaven again.

St. Francis heard: it was to him
An emblem of the Seraphim;
The upward motion of the fire,
The light, the heat, the heart's desire.

Around Assisi's convent gate
The birds, God's poor who cannot wait,
From moor and mere and darksome wood
Come flocking for their dole of food.

"O brother birds," St. Francis said,
"Ye come to me and ask for bread,
But not with bread alone to-day
Shall ye be fed and sent away.

"Ye shall be fed, ye happy birds,
With manna of celestial words;
Not mine, though mine they seem to be,
Not mine, though they be spoken through me.

"Oh, double are ye bound to praise
The great Creator in your lays;
He giveth you your plumes of down,
Your crimson hoods, your cloaks of brown.

"He giveth you your wings to fly
And breathe a purer air on high,
And careth for you everywhere,
Who for yourselves so little care!"

With flutter of swift wings and songs
Together rose the feathered throngs,
And singing scattered far apart;
Deep peace was in St. Francis' heart.

He knew not if the brotherhood
His homily had understood;
He only knew that to one ear
The meaning of his words was clear.

The Warden of the Cinque Ports

Written in October, 1852.
The Warden was the Duke of Wellington,
who died September 13.

A MIST was driving down the British Channel,
  The day was just begun,
And through the window-panes, on floor and panel,
  Streamed the red autumn sun.

It glanced on flowing flag and rippling pennon,
  And the white sails of ships;
And, from the frowning rampart, the black cannon
  Hailed it with feverish lips.

Sandwich and Romney, Hastings, Hithe, and Dover
  Were all alert that day,
To see the French war-steamers speeding over,
  When the fog cleared away.

Sullen and silent, and like couchant lions,
  Their cannon, through the night,
Holding their breath, had watched, in grim defiance,
  The sea-coast opposite.

And now they roared at drum-beat from their stations
  On every citadel;
Each answering each, with morning salutations,
  That all was well.

And down the coast, all taking up the burden,
  Replied the distant forts,

As if to summon from his sleep the Warden
  And Lord of the Cinque Ports.

Him shall no sunshine from the fields of azure,
  No drum-beat from the wall,
No morning gun from the black fort's embrasure,
  Awaken with its call!

No more, surveying with an eye impartial
  The long line of the coast,
Shall the gaunt figure of the old Field Marshal
  Be seen upon his post!

For in the night, unseen, a single warrior,
  In sombre harness mailed,
Dreaded of man, and surnamed the Destroyer,
  The rampart wall had scaled.

He passed into the chamber of the sleeper,
  The dark and silent room,
And as he entered, darker grew, and deeper,
  The silence and the gloom.

He did not pause to parley or dissemble,
  But smote the Warden hoar;
Ah! what a blow! that made all England tremble
  And groan from shore to shore.

Meanwhile, without, the surly cannon waited,
  The sun rose bright o'erhead;
Nothing in Nature's aspect intimated
  That a great man was dead.

Excelsior

THE shades of night were falling fast,
As through an Alpine village passed
A youth, who bore, 'mid snow and ice,
A banner with the strange device,
   Excelsior!

His brow was sad; his eye beneath
Flashed like a falchion from its sheath,
And like a silver clarion rung
The accents of that unknown tongue,
   Excelsior!

In happy homes he saw the light
Of household fires gleam warm and bright;
Above, the spectral glaciers shone,
And from his lips escaped a groan,
   Excelsior!

"Try not the Pass!" the old man said;
"Dark lowers the tempest overhead,
The roaring torrent is deep and wide!"
And loud that clarion voice replied,
   Excelsior!

"Oh stay," the maiden said, "and rest
Thy weary head upon this breast!"
A tear stood in his bright blue eye,
But still he answered, with a sigh,
   Excelsior!

"Beware the pine-tree's withered branch!
Beware the awful avalanche!"
This was the peasant's last Good-night,
A voice replied, far up the height,
            Excelsior!

At break of day, as heavenward
The pious monks of Saint Bernard
Uttered the oft-repeated prayer,
A voice cried through the startled air,
            Excelsior!

A traveller, by the faithful hound,
Half-buried in the snow was found,
Still grasping in his hand of ice
That banner with the strange device,
            Excelsior!

There in the twilight cold and gray,
Lifeless, but beautiful, he lay,
And from the sky, serene and far,
A voice fell, like a falling star,
            Excelsior!

The Wreck of the Hesperus

It was the schooner Hesperus,
    That sailed the wintry sea;
And the skipper had taken his little daughter,
    To bear him company.

Blue were her eyes as the fairy-flax,
    Her cheeks like the dawn of day,
And her bosom white as the hawthorn buds
    That ope in the month of May.

The skipper he stood beside the helm,
    His pipe was in his mouth,
And he watched how the veering flaw did blow
    The smoke now West, now South.

Then up and spake an old Sailor,
    Had sailed to the Spanish Main,
"I pray thee, put into yonder port,
    For I fear a hurricane.

"Last night, the moon had a golden ring,
    And tonight no moon we see!"
The skipper, he blew a whiff from his pipe,
    And a scornful laugh laughed he.

Colder and louder blew the wind,
    A gale from the Northeast,

The snow fell hissing in the brine,
  And the billows frothed like yeast.

Down came the storm, and smote amain
  The vessel in its strength;
She shuddered and paused, like a frighted steed,
  Then leaped her cable's length.

"Come hither! come hither! my little daughter,
  And do not tremble so;
For I can weather the roughest gale
  That ever wind did blow."

He wrapped her warm in his seaman's coat
  Against the stinging blast;
He cut a rope from a broken spar,
  And bound her to the mast.

"O father! I hear the church-bells ring,
  Oh say, what may it be?"
" 'Tis a fog-bell on a rock-bound coast!"—
  And he steered for the open sea.

"O father! I hear the sound of guns,
  Oh say, what may it be?"
"Some ship in distress, that cannot live
  In such an angry sea!"

"O father! I see a gleaming light,
  Oh say, what may it be?"
But the father answered never a word,
  A frozen corpse was he.

Lashed to the helm, all stiff and dark,
    With his face turned to the skies,
The lantern gleamed through the gleaming snow
    On his fixed and glassy eyes.

Then the maiden clasped her hands and prayed
    That saved she might be;
And she thought of Christ, who stilled the wave,
    On the Lake of Galilee.

And fast through the midnight dark and drear,
    Through the whistling sleet and snow,
Like a sheeted ghost, the vessel swept
    Towards the reef of Norman's Woe.

And ever the fitful gusts between
    A sound came from the land;
It was the sound of the trampling surf
    On the rocks and the hard sea-sand.

The breakers were right beneath her bows,
    She drifted a dreary wreck,
And a whooping billow swept the crew
    Like icicles from her deck.

She struck where the white and fleecy waves
    Looked soft as carded wool,
But the cruel rocks, they gored her side
    Like the horns of an angry bull.

Her rattling shrouds, all sheathed in ice,
    With the masts, went by the board;

Like a vessel of glass, she stove and sank,
    Ho! ho! the breakers roared!

At daybreak, on the bleak sea-beach,
    A fisherman stood aghast,
To see the form of a maiden fair,
    Lashed close to a drifting mast.

The salt sea was frozen on her breast,
    The salt tears in her eyes;
And he saw her hair, like the brown sea-weed,
    On the billows fall and rise.

Such was the wreck of the Hesperus,
    In the midnight and the snow!
Christ save us all from a death like this,
    On the reef of Norman's Woe!

The Village Blacksmith

UNDER a spreading chestnut-tree
   The village smithy stands;
The smith, a mighty man is he,
   With large and sinewy hands;
And the muscles of his brawny arms
   Are strong as iron bands.

His hair is crisp, and black, and long,
   His face is like the tan;
His brow is wet with honest sweat,
   He earns whate'er he can,
And looks the whole world in the face,
   For he owes not any man.

Week in, week out, from morn till night,
   You can hear his bellows blow;
You can hear him swing his heavy sledge,
   With measured beat and slow,
Like a sexton ringing the village bell,
   When the evening sun is low.

And children coming home from school
   Look in at the open door;
They love to see the flaming forge,
   And hear the bellows roar,
And catch the burning sparks that fly
   Like chaff from a threshing-floor.

He goes on Sunday to the church,
    And sits among his boys;
He hears the parson pray and preach,
    He hears his daughter's voice,
Singing in the village choir,
    And it makes his heart rejoice.

It sounds to him like her mother's voice,
    Singing in Paradise!
He needs must think of her once more,
    How in the grave she lies;
And with his hard, rough hand he wipes
    A tear out of his eyes.

Toiling,—rejoicing,—sorrowing,
    Onward through life he goes;
Each morning sees some task begin,
    Each evening sees it close;
Something attempted, something done,
    Has earned a night's repose.

Thanks, thanks to thee, my worthy friend,
    For the lesson thou hast taught!
Thus at the flaming forge of life
    Our fortunes must be wrought;
Thus on its sounding anvil shaped
    Each burning deed and thought!

POEMS OF PRINCIPLE

The Warning

Beware! The Israelite of old, who tore
  The lion in his path, — when, poor and blind,
He saw the blessed light of heaven no more,
  Shorn of his noble strength and forced to grind
In prison, and at last led forth to be
A pander to Philistine revelry, —

Upon the pillars of the temple laid
  His desperate hands, and in its overthrow
Destroyed himself, and with him those who made
  A cruel mockery of his sightless woe;
The poor, blind Slave, the scoff and jest of all,
Expired, and thousands perished in the fall!

There is a poor, blind Samson in this land,
  Shorn of his strength and bound in bonds of steel,
Who may, in some grim revel, raise his hand,
  And shake the pillars of this Commonweal,
Till the vast Temple of our liberties
A shapeless mass of wreck and rubbish lies.

The Slave Singing at Midnight

Loud he sang the psalm of David!
He, a Negro and enslaved,
Sang of Israel's victory,
Sang of Zion, bright and free.

In that hour, when night is calmest,
Sang he from the Hebrew Psalmist,
In a voice so sweet and clear
That I could not choose but hear.

Songs of triumph, and ascriptions,
Such as reached the swart Egyptians,
When upon the Red Sea coast
Perished Pharaoh and his host.

And the voice of his devotion
Filled my soul with strange emotion;
For its tones by turns were glad,
Sweetly solemn, wildly sad.

Paul and Silas, in their prison,
Sang of Christ, the Lord arisen.
And an earthquake's arm of might
Broke their dungeon-gates at night.

But, alas! what holy angel
Brings the Slave this glad evangel?
And what earthquake's arm of might
Breaks his dungeon-gates at night?

The Slave in the Dismal Swamp

In dark fens of the Dismal Swamp
   The hunted Negro lay;
He saw the fire of the midnight camp,
And heard at times a horse's tramp
   And a bloodhound's distant bay.

Where will-o'-the-wisps and glow-worms shine,
   In bulrush and in brake;
Where waving mosses shroud the pine,
And the cedar grows, and the poisonous vine
   Is spotted like the snake;

Where hardly a human foot could pass,
   Or a human heart would dare,
On the quaking turf of the green morass
He crouched in the rank and tangled grass,
   Like a wild beast in his lair.

A poor old slave, infirm and lame;
   Great scars deformed his face;
On his forehead he bore the brand of shame,
And the rags, that hid his mangled frame,
   Were the livery of disgrace.

All things above were bright and fair,
   All things were glad and free;
Lithe squirrels darted here and there,
And wild birds filled the echoing air
   With songs of Liberty!

On him alone was the doom of pain,
  From the morning of his birth;
On him alone the curse of Cain
Fell, like a flail on the garnered grain,
  And struck him to the earth!

The Jewish Cemetery at Newport

How strange it seems! These Hebrews in their graves,
  Close by the street of this fair seaport town,
Silent beside the never-silent waves,
  At rest in all this moving up and down!

The trees are white with dust, that o'er their sleep
  Wave their broad curtains in the south-wind's breath,
While underneath these leafy tents they keep
  The long, mysterious Exodus of Death.

And these sepulchral stones, so old and brown,
  That pave with level flags their burial-place,
Seem like the tablets of the Law, thrown down
  And broken by Moses at the mountain's base.

The very names recorded here are strange.
  Of foreign accent, and of different climes;
Alvares and Rivera interchange
  With Abraham and Jacob of old times.

"Blessed be God, for he created Death!"
  The mourners said, "and Death is rest and peace";
Then added, in the certainty of faith,
  "And giveth Life that nevermore shall cease."

Closed are the portals of their Synagogue,
  No Psalms of David now the silence break,
No Rabbi reads the ancient Decalogue
  In the grand dialect the Prophets spake.

Gone are the living, but the dead remain,
　　And not neglected; for a hand unseen,
Scattering its bounty, like a summer rain,
　　Still keeps their graves and their remembrance green.

How came they here? What burst of Christian hate,
　　What persecution, merciless and blind,
Drove o'er the sea — that desert desolate —
　　These Ishmaels and Hagars of mankind?

They lived in narrow streets and lanes obscure,
　　Ghetto and Judenstrass, in mirk and mire;
Taught in the school of patience to endure
　　The life of anguish and the death of fire.

All their lives long, with the unleavened bread
　　And bitter herbs of exile and its fears,
The wasting famine of the heart they fed,
　　And slaked its thirst with marah of their tears.

Anathema maranatha! was the cry
　　That rang from town to town, from street to street:
At every gate the accursed Mordecai
　　Was mocked and jeered, and spurned by Christian feet.

Pride and humiliation hand in hand
　　Walked with them through the world where'er they
　　　　went;
Trampled and beaten were they as the sand,
　　And yet unshaken as the continent.

For in the background figures vague and vast
    Of patriarchs and of prophets rose sublime,
And all the great traditions of the Past
    They saw reflected in the coming time.

And thus forever with reverted look
    The mystic volume of the world they read,
Spelling it backward, like a Hebrew book,
    Till life became a Legend of the Dead.

But ah! what once has been shall be no more!
    The groaning earth in travail and in pain
Brings forth its races, but does not restore,
    And the dead nations never rise again.

The Arsenal at Springfield

THIS is the Arsenal. From floor to ceiling,
  Like a huge organ, rise the burnished arms;
But from their silent pipes no anthem pealing
  Startles the villages with strange alarms.

Ah! what a sound will rise, how wild and dreary,
  When the death-angel touches those swift keys!
What loud lament and dismal Miserere
  Will mingle with their awful symphonies!

I hear even now the infinite fierce chorus,
  The cries of agony, the endless groan,
Which, through the ages that have gone before us,
  In long reverberations reach our own.

On helm and harness rings the Saxon hammer,
  Through Cimbric forest roars the Norseman's song.
And loud, amid the universal clamor,
  O'er distant deserts sounds the Tartar gong.

I hear the Florentine, who from his palace
  Wheels out his battle-bell with dreadful din,
And Aztec priests upon their teocallis
  Beat the wild war-drums made of serpent's skin;

The tumult of each sacked and burning village;
  The shout that every prayer for mercy drowns;
The soldiers' revels in the midst of pillage;
  The wail of famine in beleaguered towns;

The bursting shell, the gateway wrenched asunder,
  The rattling musketry, the clashing blade;
And ever and anon, in tones of thunder
  The diapason of the cannonade.

Is it, O man, with such discordant noises,
  With such accursed instruments as these,
Thou drownest Nature's sweet and kindly voices,
  And jarrest the celestial harmonies?

Were half the power, that fills the world with terror,
  Were half the wealth, bestowed on camps and
    courts,
Given to redeem the human mind from error,
  There were no need of arsenals or forts:

The warrior's name would be a name abhorrèd!
  And every nation, that should lift again
Its hand against a brother, on its forehead
  Would wear forevermore the curse of Cain!

Down the dark future, through long generations,
  The echoing sounds grow fainter and then cease;
And like a bell, with solemn, sweet vibrations,
  I hear once more the voice of Christ say, "Peace!"

Peace! and no longer from its brazen portals
  The blast of War's great organ shakes the skies!
But beautiful as songs of the immortals,
  The holy melodies of love arise.

The Occultation of Orion

I saw, as in a dream sublime,
The balance in the hand of Time.
O'er East and West its beam impended;
And day, with all its hours of light,
Was slowly sinking out of sight,
While opposite, the scale of night
Silently with the stars ascended.

Like the astrologers of eld,
In that bright vision I beheld
Greater and deeper mysteries.
I saw, with its celestial keys,
Its chords of air, its frets of fire,
The Samian's great Aeolian lyre,
Rising through all its sevenfold bars,
From earth unto the fixed stars,
And through the dewy atmosphere,
Not only could I see, but hear,
Its wondrous and harmonious strings,
In sweet vibration, sphere by sphere,
From Dian's circle light and near,
Onward to vaster and wider rings,
Where, chanting through his beard of snows,
Majestic, mournful, Saturn goes,
And down the sunless realms of space
Reverberates the thunder of his bass.

Beneath the sky's triumphal arch
This music sounded like a march,

And with its chorus seemed to be
Preluding some great tragedy.
Sirius was rising in the east;
And, slow ascending one by one,
The kindling constellations shone.
Begirt with many a blazing star,
Stood the great giant Algebar,
Orion, hunter of the beast!
His sword hung gleaming by his side,
And, on his arm, the lion's hide
Scattered across the midnight air
The golden radiance of its hair.

The moon was pallid, but not faint;
And beautiful as some fair saint,
Serenely moving on her way
In hours of trial and dismay.
As if she heard the voice of God,
Unharmed with naked feet she trod
Upon the hot and burning stars,
As on the glowing coals and bars,
That were to prove her strength, and try
Her holiness and her purity.

Thus moving on, with silent pace,
And triumph in her sweet, pale face,
She reached the station of Orion.
Aghast he stood in strange alarm!
And suddenly from his outstretched arm
Down fell the red skin of the lion
Into the river at his feet.
His mighty club no longer beat

The forehead of the bull; but he
Reeled as of yore beside the sea,
When, blinded by Oenopion,
He sought the blacksmith at his forge,
And, climbing up the mountain gorge,
Fixed his blank eyes upon the sun.

Then, through the silence overhead,
An angel with a trumpet said,
"Forevermore, forevermore,
The reign of violence is o'er!"
And, like an instrument that flings
Its music on another's strings,
The trumpet of the angel cast
Upon the heavenly lyre its blast,
And on from sphere to sphere the words
Re-echoed down the burning chords,—
"Forevermore, forevermore,
The reign of violence is o'er!"

In the Churchyard at Cambridge

In the village churchyard she lies,
Dust in her beautiful eyes,
    No more she breathes, nor feels, nor stirs;
At her feet and at her head
Lies a slave to attend the dead,
    But their dust is white as hers.

Was she, a lady of high degree,
So much in love with the vanity
    And foolish pomp of this world of ours?
Or was it Christian charity,
And lowliness and humility,
    The richest and rarest of all dowers?

Who shall tell us? No one speaks;
No color shoots into those cheeks,
    Either of anger or of pride,
At the rude question we have asked;
Nor will the mystery be unmasked
    By those who are sleeping at her side.

Hereafter?—And do you think to look
On the terrible pages of that Book
    To find her failings, faults, and errors?
Ah, you will then have other cares,
In your own shortcomings and despairs,
    In your own secret sins and terrors!

SONNETS

Chaucer

AN old man in a lodge within a park;
   The chamber walls depicted all around
   With portraitures of huntsman, hawk, and hound,
   And the hurt deer. He listeneth to the lark,
Whose song comes with the sunshine through the dark
   Of painted glass in leaden lattice bound;
   He listeneth and he laugheth at the sound,
   Then writeth in a book like any clerk.
He is the poet of the dawn, who wrote
   The Canterbury Tales, and his old age
   Made beautiful with song; and as I read
I hear the crowing cock, I hear the note
   Of lark and linnet, and from every page
   Rise odors of ploughed field or flowery mead.

The Old Bridge at Florence

TADDEO Gaddi built me. I am old,
    Five centuries old. I plant my foot of stone
    Upon the Arno, as St. Michael's own
    Was planted on the dragon. Fold by fold
Beneath me as it struggles, I behold
    Its glistening scales. Twice hath it overthrown
    My kindred and companions. Me alone
    It moveth not, but is by me controlled.
I can remember when the Medici
    Were driven from Florence; longer still ago
    The final wars of Ghibelline and Guelf.
Florence adorns me with her jewelry;
    And when I think that Michael Angelo
    Hath leaned on me, I glory in myself.

Dante

Tuscan, that wanderest through the realms of
    gloom.
    With thoughtful pace, and sad, majestic eyes,
    Stern thoughts and awful from thy soul arise,
    Like Farinata from his fiery tomb.
Thy sacred song is like the trump of doom;
    Yet in thy heart what human sympathies,
    What soft compassion glows, as in the skies
    The tender stars their clouded lamps relume!
Methinks I see thee stand, with pallid cheeks,
    By Fra Hilario in his diocese,
    As up the convent-walls, in golden streaks,
The ascending sunbeams mark the day's decrease;
    And, as he asks what there the stranger seeks,
    Thy voice along the cloister whispers "Peace!"

I

Oft have I seen at some cathedral door
  A laborer, pausing in the dust and heat,
  Lay down his burden, and with reverent feet
  Enter, and cross himself, and on the floor
Kneel to repeat his paternoster o'er;
  Far off the noises of the world retreat;
  The loud vociferations of the street
  Become an undistinguishable roar.
So, as I enter here from day to day,
  And leave my burden at this minster gate,
  Kneeling in prayer, and not ashamed to pray,
The tumult of the time disconsolate
  To inarticulate murmurs dies away,
  While the eternal ages watch and wait.

II

How strange the sculptures that adorn these towers!
  This crowd of statues, in whose folded sleeves
  Birds build their nests; while canopied with leaves
  Parvis and portal bloom like trellised bowers,
And the vast minster seems a cross of flowers!
  But fiends and dragons on the gargoyled eaves
  Watch the dead Christ between the living thieves,
  And, underneath, the traitor Judas lowers!
Ah! from what agonies of heart and brain,
  What exultations trampling on despair,
  What tenderness, what tears, what hate of wrong,

What passionate outcry of a soul in pain,
   Uprose this poem of the earth and air,
   This mediaeval miracle of song!

III

I enter, and I see thee in the gloom
   Of the long aisles, O poet saturnine!
   And strive to make my steps keep pace with thine.
   The air is filled with some unknown perfume;
The congregation of the dead make room
   For thee to pass; the votive tapers shine;
   Like rooks that haunt Ravenna's groves of pine
   The hovering echoes fly from tomb to tomb.
From the confessionals I hear arise
   Rehearsals of forgotten tragedies,
   And lamentations from the crypts below;
And then a voice celestial that begins
   With the pathetic words, "Although your sins
   As scarlet be," and ends with "as the snow."

IV

With snow-white veil and garments as of flame,
   She stands before thee, who so long ago
   Filled thy young heart with passion and the woe
   From which thy song and all its splendors came.
And while with stern rebuke she speaks thy name,
   The ice about thy heart melts as the snow
   On mountain heights, and in swift overflow
   Comes gushing from thy lips in sobs of shame.
Thou makest full confession; and a gleam,

As of the dawn on some dark forest cast,
    Seems on thy lifted forehead to increase;
Lethe and Eunoë—the remembered dream
    And the forgotten sorrow—bring at last
    That perfect pardon which is perfect peace.

V

I lift mine eyes, and all the windows blaze
    With forms of Saints and holy men who died,
    Here martyred and hereafter glorified;
    And the great Rose upon its leaves displays
Christ's Triumph, and the angelic roundelays,
    With splendor upon splendor multiplied;
    And Beatrice again at Dante's side
    No more rebukes, but smiles her words of praise.
And then the organ sounds, and unseen choirs
    Sing the old Latin hymns of peace and love
    And benedictions of the Holy Ghost;
And the melodious bells among the spires
    O'er all the house-tops and through heaven above
    Proclaim the elevation of the Host!

VI

O star of morning and of liberty!
    O bringer of the light, whose splendor shines
    Above the darkness of the Apennines,
    Forerunner of the day that is to be!
The voices of the city and the sea,
    The voices of the mountains and the pines,
    Repeat thy song, till the familiar lines
    Are footpaths for the thought of Italy!

Thy flame is blown abroad from all the heights,
  Through all the nations, and a sound is heard,
  As of a mighty wind, and men devout,
Strangers of Rome, and the new proselytes
  In their own language hear thy wondrous word,
  And many are amazed and many doubt.

The Sound of the Sea

THE sea awoke at midnight from its sleep,
  And round the pebbly beaches far and wide
  I heard the first wave of the rising tide
  Rush onward with uninterrupted sweep;
A voice out of the silence of the deep,
  A sound mysteriously multiplied
  As of a cataract from the mountain's side,
  Or roar of winds upon a wooded steep.
So comes to us at times, from the unknown
  And inaccessible solitudes of being,
  The rushing of the sea-tides of the soul;
And inspirations, that we deem our own,
  Are some divine foreshadowing and foreseeing
  Of things beyond our reason or control.

The Tides

I saw the long line of the vacant shore,
  The sea-weed and the shells upon the sand,
  And the brown rocks left bare on every hand,
  As if the ebbing tide would flow no more.
Then heard I, more distinctly than before,
  The ocean breathe and its great breast expand,
  And hurrying came on the defenceless land
  The insurgent waters with tumultuous roar.
All thought and feeling and desire, I said,
  Love, laughter, and the exultant joy of song
  Have ebbed from me forever! Suddenly o'er me
They swept again from their deep ocean bed,
  And in a tumult of delight, and strong
  As youth, and beautiful as youth, upbore me.

Mezzo Cammin

HALF of my life is gone, and I have let
   The years slip from me and have not fulfilled
   The aspiration of my youth, to build
   Some tower of song with lofty parapet.
Not indolence, nor pleasure, nor the fret
   Of restless passions that would not be stilled,
   But sorrow, and a care that almost killed,
   Kept me from what I may accomplish yet;
Though half-way up the hill, I see the Past
   Lying beneath me with its sounds and sights,—
   A city in the twilight dim and vast,
With smoking roofs, soft bells, and gleaming
     lights,—
   And hear above me on the autumnal blast
   The cataract of Death far thundering from the
     heights.

The Broken Oar

ONCE upon Iceland's solitary strand
    A poet wandered with his book and pen,
    Seeking some final word, some sweet Amen,
    Wherewith to close the volume in his hand.
The billows rolled and plunged upon the sand,
    The circling sea-gulls swept beyond his ken,
    And from the parting cloud-rack now and then
    Flashed the red sunset over sea and land.
Then by the billows at his feet was tossed
    A broken oar; and carved thereon he read:
    "Oft was I weary, when I toiled at thee";
And like a man, who findeth what was lost,
    He wrote the words, then lifted up his head,
    And flung his useless pen into the sea.

The Cross of Snow

In the long, sleepless watches of the night,
   A gentle face — the face of one long dead —
   Looks at me from the wall, where round its head
   The night-lamp casts a halo of pale light.
Here in this room she died; and soul more white
   Never through martyrdom of fire was led
   To its repose; nor can in books be read
   The legend of a life more benedight.
There is a mountain in the distant West
   That, sun-defying, in its deep ravines
   Displays a cross of snow upon its side.
Such is the cross I wear upon my breast
   These eighteen years, through all the changing scenes
   And seasons, changeless since the day she died.

EXCERPTS FROM
MICHAEL ANGELO
A FRAGMENT

DEDICATION

Nothing that is shall perish utterly,
  But perish only to revive again
  In other forms, as clouds restore in rain
  The exhalations of the land and sea.
Men build their houses from the masonry
  Of ruined tombs; the passion and the pain
  Of hearts, that long have ceased to beat, remain
  To throb in hearts that are, or are to be.
So from old chronicles, where sleep in dust
  Names that once filled the world with trumpet tones,
  I build this verse; and flowers of song have thrust
Their roots among the loose disjointed stones,
  Which to this end I fashion as I must.
  Quickened are they that touch the Prophet's bones.

————

MONOLOGUE: THE LAST JUDGMENT

*Michael Angelo's Studio. He is at work
on the cartoon of the Last Judgment.*

MICHAEL ANGELO.

  Why did the Pope and his ten Cardinals
  Come here to lay this heavy task upon me?
  Were not the paintings on the Sistine ceiling
  Enough for them? They saw the Hebrew leader
  Waiting, and clutching his tempestuous beard,
  But heeded not. The bones of Julius
  Shook in their sepulchre. I heard the sound;
  They only heard the sound of their own voices.

Are there no other artists here in Rome
To do this work, that they must needs seek me?
Fra Bastian, my Fra Bastian, might have done it,
But he is lost to art. The Papal Seals,
Like leaden weights upon a dead man's eyes,
Press down his lids; and so the burden falls
On Michael Angelo, Chief Architect
And Painter of the Apostolic Palace.
That is the title they cajole me with,
To make me do their work and leave my own;
But having once begun, I turn not back.
Blow, ye bright angels, on your golden trumpets
To the four corners of the earth, and wake
The dead to judgment! Ye recording angels,
Open your books and read! Ye dead, awake!
Rise from your graves, drowsy and drugged with death,
As men who suddenly aroused from sleep
Look round amazed, and know not where they are!

In happy hours, when the imagination
Wakes like a wind at midnight, and the soul
Trembles in all its leaves, it is a joy
To be uplifted on its wings, and listen
To the prophetic voices in the air
That call us onward. Then the work we do
Is a delight, and the obedient hand
Never grows weary. But how different is it
In the disconsolate, discouraged hours,
When all the wisdom of the world appears
As trivial as the gossip of a nurse
In a sick-room, and all our work seems useless.

SAN SILVESTRO

MICHAEL ANGELO.
                    Ah, to build, to build!
That is the noblest art of all the arts.
Painting and sculpture are but images,
Are merely shadows cast by outward things
On stone or canvas, having in themselves
No separate existence. Architecture,
Existing in itself, and not in seeming
A something it is not, surpasses them
As substance shadow. Long, long years ago,
Standing one morning near the Baths of Titus,
I saw the statue of Laocoön
Rise from its grave of centuries, like a ghost
Writhing in pain; and as it tore away
The knotted serpents from its limbs, I heard,
Or seemed to hear, the cry of agony
From its white, parted lips. And still I marvel
At the three Rhodian artists, by whose hands
This miracle was wrought. Yet he beholds
Far nobler works who looks upon the ruins
Of temples in the Forum here in Rome.
If God should give me power in my old age
To build for Him a temple half as grand
As those were in their glory, I should count
My age more excellent than youth itself,
And all that I have hitherto accomplished
As only vanity.

VITTORIA COLONNA.

I understand you.
Art is the gift of God, and must be used
Unto His glory. That in art is highest
Which aims at this. . . .

———

MICHAEL ANGELO. (*Opening the* Divina Commedia)

I turn for consolation to the leaves
Of the great master of our Tuscan tongue,
Whose words, like colored garnet-shirls in lava,
Betray the heat in which they were engendered.
A mendicant, he ate the bitter bread
Of others, but repaid their meagre gifts
With immortality. In courts of princes
He was a by-word, and in streets of towns
Was mocked by children, like the Hebrew
    prophet,
Himself a prophet. I too know the cry,
Go up, thou bald head! from a generation
That, wanting reverence, wanteth the best food
The soul can feed on. There's not room enough
For age and youth upon this little planet.
Age must give way. There was not room enough
Even for this great poet. In his song
I hear reverberate the gates of Florence,
Closing upon him, never more to open;
But mingled with the sound are melodies
Celestial from the gates of paradise.
He came and he is gone. The people knew not
What manner of man was passing by their doors,

Until he passed no more; but in his vision
He saw the torments and beatitudes
Of souls condemned or pardoned, and hath left
Behind him this sublime Apocalypse.

———

MICHAEL ANGELO.

The work is nearly done. But this Last Judgment
Has been the cause of more vexation to me
Than it will be of honor. Ser Biagio,
Master of ceremonies at the Papal court,
A man punctilious and over nice,
Calls it improper; says that those nude forms,
Showing their nakedness in such shameless fashion,
Are better suited to a common bagnio,
Or wayside wine-shop, than a Papal Chapel.
To punish him I painted him as Minos
And leave him there as master of ceremonies
In the Infernal Regions. What would you
Have done to such a man?

———

MICHAEL ANGELO.

. . . I sometimes fear
That, when we die, with us all art will die.
'T is but a fancy. Nature will provide
Others to take our places. I rejoice
To see the young spring forward in the race,
Eager as we were, and as full of hope
And the sublime audacity of youth.

[*149*]

TITIAN.

Men die and are forgotten. The great world
Goes on the same. Among the myriads
Of men that live, or have lived, or shall live,
What is a single life, or thine or mine,
That we should think all nature would stand still
If we were gone? We must make room for others.

———————

MICHAEL ANGELO. (*In the Coliseum*)

Behold

How wonderful it is! The queen of flowers,
The marble rose of Rome! Its petals torn
By wind and rain of thrice five hundred years;
Its mossy sheath half rent away, and sold
To ornament our palaces and churches,
Or to be trodden under feet of man
Upon the Tiber's bank; yet what remains
Still opening its fair bosom to the sun,
And to the constellations that at night
Hang poised above it like a swarm of bees.

———————

MICHAEL ANGELO.

Oh, I am put to shame, when I consider
How mean our work is, when compared with theirs!
Look at these walls about us and above us!
They have been shaken by earthquakes, have
        been made

A fortress, and been battered by long sieges;
The iron clamps, that held the stones together,
Have been wrenched from them; but they stand
    erect
And firm, as if they had been hewn and hollowed
Out of the solid rock, and were a part
Of the foundations of the world itself.

                    .   .   .   .

        A thousand wild flowers bloom
From every chink, and the birds build their nests
Among the ruined arches, and suggest
New thoughts of beauty to the architect.
Now let us climb the broken stairs that lead
Into the corridors above, and study
The marvel and the mystery of that art
In which I am a pupil, not a master.

All things must have an end; the world itself
Must have an end, as in a dream I saw it.
There came a great hand out of heaven, and
    touched
The earth, and stopped it in its course. The
    seas
Leaped, a vast cataract, into the abyss;
The forests and the fields slid off, and
    floated
Like wooded islands in the air. The dead
Were hurled forth from their sepulchres; the
    living
Were mingled with them, and themselves were
    dead,—

All being dead; and the fair, shining cities
Dropped out like jewels from a broken crown.
Naught but the core of the great globe remained,
A skeleton of stone. And over it
The wrack of matter drifted like a cloud,
And then recoiled upon itself, and fell
Back on the empty world, that with the weight
Reeled, staggered, righted, and then headlong
    plunged
Into the darkness, as a ship, when struck
By a great sea, throws off the waves at first
On either side, then settles and goes down
Into the dark abyss, with her dead crew.

————

MICHAEL ANGELO.

All liberty is dead. Ah, woe is me!
I hoped to see my country rise to heights
Of happiness and freedom yet unreached
By other nations, but the climbing wave
Pauses, lets go its hold, and slides again
Back to the common level, with a hoarse
Death-rattle in its throat. I am too old
To hope for better days. I will stay here
And die in Rome. The very weeds, that grow
Among the broken fragments of her ruins,
Are sweeter to me than the garden flowers
Of other cities; and the desolate ring

Of the Campagna round about her walls
Fairer than all the villas that encircle
The towns of Tuscany.

————

BENVENUTO CELLINI.

Sculpture is more divine, and more like Nature,
That fashions all her works in high relief,
And that is sculpture. This vast ball, the Earth,
Was moulded out of clay, and baked in fire;
Men, women, and all animals that breathe
Are statues and not paintings. Even the plants,
The flowers, the fruits, the grasses, were first
    sculptured,
And colored later. Painting is a lie,
A shadow merely.

MICHAEL ANGELO.

                    Truly, as you say,
Sculpture is more than painting. It is greater
To raise the dead to life than to create
Phantoms that seem to live. The most majestic
Of the three sister arts is that which builds;
The eldest of them all, to whom the others
Are but the handmaids and the servitors,
Being but imitation, not creation.
Henceforth I dedicate myself to her.

————

MICHAEL ANGELO.

                    Some have eyes.
That see not; but in every block of marble
I see a statue,—see it as distinctly
As if it stood before me shaped and perfect
In attitude and action. I have only
To hew away the stone walls that imprison
The lovely apparition, and reveal it
To other eyes as mine already see it.

INDEX OF TITLES

INDEX OF TITLES

INDEX OF FIRST LINES

INDEX OF FIRST LINES

ABOUT EDMUND FULLER

Edmund Fuller is an author, editor, critic, and teacher. He has written three novels: *A Star Pointed North, Brothers Divided,* and *The Corridor.* His diversified nonfiction includes *Man in Modern Fiction* and *Books with Men Behind Them.* His reviews and articles have appeared in *The New York Times,* the *Wall Street Journal,* the *New York Herald Tribune,* the *Chicago Tribune,* the *American Scholar, Saturday Review,* and *Horizon.* He has taught at Columbia University, Kent School, and St. Stephen's School, Rome. In the field of textbooks he is co-author of *Adventures in American Literature* and general editor of the series *Adventures in Good Books.*

ABOUT THE ARTISTS

Clare Romano Ross and John Ross are graduates of the Cooper Union School of Art and have studied at the Ecole des Beaux Arts at Fontainbleau and the Instituto Statale in Florence. The Rosses were awarded Tiffany Fellowships for printmaking and lived in Italy for a year while Mrs. Ross had a Fulbright grant. They were artists in residence with the U.S.I.A. exhibition, "Graphic Arts, U.S.A." in Romania and Yugoslavia, where they traveled extensively, giving lectures and demonstrations.

They are represented in museums throughout the United States and their work is in the permanent collection of the Metropolitan Museum of Art. Clare and John Ross are also on the faculties of Pratt Institute, Manhattanville College, and the New School for Social Research.